Building American Submarines

CONTRIBUTIONS TO NAVAL HISTORY . . . NO. 3

Building American
Submarines, 1914-1940

Gary E. Weir

Naval Historical Center
Department of the Navy
Washington, D.C. 1991

Library of Congress Cataloging-in-Publication Data

Weir, Gary E.
    Building American submarines, 1914–1940 / Gary E. Weir.
      p. cm. — (Contributions to naval history ; no. 3)
    Includes bibliographical references and index.
    ISBN 0–945274–04–1
    1. Submarine boats—United States—History.   I. Title.
II. Series.
V858.W45   1991   90–23605
623.8'2572'0973—dc20

For sale by the Superintendent of Documents, U.S. Government Printing Office
Washington, D.C. 20402

To my six-year-old daughter
Lili
who constantly reminds me that
it is more important to go for a walk in the park

Contributions to Naval History Series

Michael A. Palmer, *Origins of the Maritime Strategy:*
American Naval Strategy in the First Postwar Decade   1988

Thomas C. Hone, *Power and Change: The Administrative*
History of the Office of the Chief of Naval Operations,
1946–1986   1989

Gary E. Weir, *Building American Submarines,*
1914–1940   1991

Tamara Moser Melia, *"Damn the Torpedoes": A Short*
History of U.S. Naval Mine Countermeasures,
1777–1991   forthcoming

Michael A. Palmer, *The United States Navy*
and the Persian Gulf   forthcoming

Jeffrey G. Barlow, *The "Revolt of the Admirals":*
The Postwar Fight for Naval Aviation   forthcoming

The Author

Dr. Gary E. Weir has worked as a historian with the Contemporary History Branch of the Naval Historical Center since 1987. He studied under Professor John H. Morrow, Jr., at the University of Tennessee, Knoxville, earning his doctorate in history in 1982. In the winter of 1991, Naval Institute Press will publish Dr. Weir's history of the construction of the German High Seas Fleet under the title, *Building the Kaiser's Navy: The Imperial Naval Office and German Industry in the Tirpitz Era, 1890–1919*. His work has also appeared in *Military Affairs, International History Review*, U.S. Naval Institute *Proceedings, Naval History*, and the *Naval Engineers Journal*. He is currently writing an official history on the naval-industrial relations governing American submarine construction from 1940 to 1960.

Foreword

In this volume, Gary E. Weir assesses the Navy's efforts between 1914 and 1940 to develop effective submarines. In particular, the author describes the work of the Navy and private industry that allowed the relatively primitive submersible of the First World War period to be replaced by the fleet submarine that fought in the Second World War.

Building American Submarines argues that there was a fundamental shift in the relationship between the Navy and its submarine suppliers during this period. After being completely dependent upon private industry in 1914, the Navy—not industry—controlled the design and construction process by the eve of the Second World War. As a result, the Navy was able to acquire high-quality submarines to fulfill the nation's strategic requirements. When we entered the Second World War, these new submarines were ready to undertake prolonged and effective antishipping operations in distant waters. That capability was of enormous importance in the ensuing triumph of American sea power over Imperial Japan.

In tracing these developments, the author provides insights into the goals of the naval submarine leaders, the evolution of the American submarine industry, the influence of German underseas technology, and strategic requirements foreseen by naval planners. The Navy's historians hope that this case study of the problems and successes involved in a major weapons acquisition program will be of particular interest to naval personnel involved in that process today, as well as to representatives of the industrial firms that supply the needs of the modern Navy.

Many people assisted Dr. Weir as he completed this history. I especially wish to thank Dr. Edward J. Marolda, Head of the Naval Historical Center's Contemporary History Branch, who managed the project from its outset. Our dedicated senior editor, Sandra Doyle, skillfully steered the manuscript through the editorial and publication process. Several scholars noted for their work in the history of technology generously reviewed the manuscript and offered their comments. They include Commander John D. Alden, USN (Ret.), author of several works on submarine history; Dr. Francis Duncan, an authority on the nuclear Navy; Professor I. B. Holley of Duke University; and Dr. William N. Still of East Carolina University.

While valuable comments and assistance were received from these and other individuals, the opinions and conclusions expressed in this history are solely those of Dr. Weir. They do not reflect the views of the Department of the Navy or of any other agency of the U.S. Government.

Dean C. Allard
Director of Naval History

Acknowledgments

In 1987 when the research for this study began as the first part of a much larger project, I contacted Captain Harry Jackson, USN (Ret.), one of the Navy's best and most innovative submarine engineers and designers. Captain Jackson graciously replied to my letter and told me I was embarking on a long and arduous voyage that I would find both challenging and rewarding. He was correct on both counts.

Although I confess to a life-long fascination with submarines, the energy and enthusiasm required to complete a study of this sort cannot be sustained merely by one man's interest in the subject. Therefore I would like to thank Captain Jackson for his kindness, his time, and his efforts to inform and teach. Similar thanks must go to other officers who helped in exactly the same way: Rear Admiral Albert G. Mumma, USN (Ret.); Rear Admiral Robert L. Moore, USN (Ret.); Captain William Roseborough, USN (Ret.); and Captain Henry Arnold, USN (Ret.).

On the civilian side, Mr. Jack Leonard and Mr. Frank Horan, both retired officials of the Electric Boat Division of General Dynamics Corporation, kindly made time for my questions on engineering matters and industry's relationship with the Navy. Mr. James F. Blose and Dr. Laskar Wechsler provided important insights after having read a portion of this study, which was presented at the annual meeting of the American Society of Naval Engineers in May 1989. I would also like to thank Mr. Neil Runzel, public affairs officer for the Electric Boat Division, and Mr. Charles Giles of the company's Technical Library for their cooperation and assistance. Dr. Ronald Spector, the former Director of Naval History, initially approved this project and the current Director of Naval History, Dr. Dean C. Allard, has supported and nurtured the study with insight and advice for which I am grateful.

Dr. Edward J. Marolda, Head of the Contemporary History Branch, offered much needed guidance, support, and editorial expertise, and our editor Ms. Sandra Doyle, as always, deftly guided the manuscript through final editing and publication. The professional staff of SSR, Inc., skillfully handled the substantive editing and indexing of the book. The manuscript also benefitted from the comments of my colleagues Drs. Jeffrey G. Barlow, Theresa L. Kraus, and Michael A. Palmer. Mr. Robert Cressman of the Ships' Histories Branch offered valuable insights into the interwar Navy and the personality and importance of Admiral Yarnell. Mr. Charles Haberlein of the Naval Historical Center's Photographic Section provided excellent technical and historical advice.

I am also indebted to a number of excellent archivists, who deciphered finding aids, located collections, and momentarily put aside what they were doing to further my work. These include Mr. Barry Zerby, Mr. Richard von Doehnhoff, and Mr. Richard Boylan of the National Archives; Ms. Kathleen Lloyd, Mr. Michael Walker, Mr. Bernard Cavalcante, and Ms. Kathleen Rohr of the U.S. Navy's Operational Archives; Ms. Theresa Cass of the Submarine Force Library and Museum in Groton, Connecticut; and Mr. Wes Pryce of the David Taylor Research Center.

The support of the Navy Department Library was also essential, and for their consistent enthusiastic support I would like to thank Mr. John Vajda and Mr. Dale Sharrick.

The production staff of *Naval Aviation News* deserves special thanks, particularly Journalist Chief James G. Richeson and Ms. Joan A. Frasher for the typesetting and Mr. Charles C. Cooney for the design and layout of this book.

At home my wife, Catherine, and my daughter, Lili, helped me keep history and submarines in proper perspective. They gave me love, time, and advice, and reminded me that there are other marvelous things in life even more important than history.

It only remains to be said that any opinions and errors of fact or interpretation that appear on the following pages are my own and do not reflect or represent the views of the Department of the Navy or the Naval Historical Center.

Gary E. Weir

Contents

Illustrations

Photographs with NH numbers are held by the Naval Historical Center, Washington, D.C. 20374–0571.

Introduction

In most historical and technical treatments of the American submarine, the formative period of the U.S. Navy's association with the submarine industry is virtually ignored. This study is the first step in a comprehensive effort to fill that void. Covering the period 1914–1940, this study places issues of submarine technology, design, and construction in the wider context of the naval-industrial relationship that governed production. The importance of this association went beyond assembling submarines. The perspectives and prejudices brought to this partnership by naval officers and industrial leaders alike fashioned the environment within which American submarines have evolved since the Great War of 1914–1918.

The analysis offered here does not present a monolithic or static view of the naval-industrial complex and its antecedents. Rather than growing out of a single historical event or political-economic entity, this partnership between industry and the Navy emerged as a network of independent relationships developing simultaneously. Each was based upon the historical timing and complexity of the particular vessel and technology involved. The common motives of national defense, mutual growth, and profit bonded all of these individual components into the naval-industrial complex. Although a relationship of this sort developed as early as the 1880s and governed the fabrication of surface vessels in the United States, nothing comparable existed for the construction of submarines before the Great War. Instead, an effective relationship gradually developed between 1914 and 1940, setting the stage for the emergence of a naval-industrial complex for submarines during the Second World War.

As it is used here, the term naval-industrial complex depends heavily upon Samuel P. Huntington's definition of the military-industrial complex.[1] He characterized this elusive and often misunderstood component of Western society and economy as "a large permanent military establishment supported by and linked to a variety of related industrial, labor, and geographical interests."

His description provides an understandable conceptual framework for this study and offers an excellent opportunity to explore the transition of the private-public relationship from the simple interaction between buyer and seller to the advent of a naval-industrial complex for submarines. It also creates an environment for inquiry flexible enough to permit discussion of the different motives and goals of the participants and the changing roles of the

Navy and industry that contributed to the evolution of the naval-industrial complex.

The term "submarine" is universally used in this book in spite of the fact that all of the vessels discussed in these pages are actually "submersibles." The first true submarine was USS *Nautilus* (SSN–571), a vessel that did not depend on surface air and could, at least in theory, remain submerged for an indefinite period limited only by the endurance of her crew.

Even before American entry into the First World War in 1917, the Navy depended heavily upon private industry to provide submarine designs, advanced technology, and construction capability. Between the two world wars, however, the tables turned completely. Rather than complete dependence upon firms like the Electric Boat Company, the bureaus attained a level of technical expertise in design and construction equivalent to the best that private industry had to offer. On the eve of Pearl Harbor the expertise and experience accrued by the Navy during the interwar years combined with the contracting authority of the naval bureaus and the Secretary of the Navy to transform the Navy into the dominant partner in its relationship with the submarine industry.

Historian William McNeill has described this relationship in its often turbulent early stages, as one of "command technology." At the turn of the century, industry built larger, faster, and more powerful ships in direct response to the special demands of naval leaders like Admiral Sir John Fisher, Great Britain's First Sea Lord; Admiral Alfred von Tirpitz, Chief of the German Imperial Naval Office; and Admiral George Dewey, Chairman of the U.S. Navy's General Board.[2] Instead of allowing the private sector to develop more effective engines of war in response to international market forces, these naval leaders now ordered specific weapons and technologies to support preferred naval strategies and policies. In developing these command technologies, the armaments industries and the navies of the major Western powers inaugurated a relationship that represented the first stage in the evolution of the naval-industrial complex.[3]

During the interwar period, command technologies for highly specialized naval products like submarines emerged very slowly in both Europe and the United States because of restricted competition or outright monopoly. Frequently the private sector first developed and then controlled the advanced naval technologies essential to the fabrication of these products. Thus companies that pioneered important innovations could determine the technical alternatives open to the Navy, new directions in research and development, and the price of the final product.

Given these circumstances and the absence of a nonmilitary market for submarines, American naval leaders tried to encourage competition. In the process they precipitated a struggle for control of the technology, market, and price between the Navy and some of its most important contractors. Naval officers frequently expressed frustration with what they perceived as the self-serving motives of industry. Industrial leaders, in turn, found themselves defending their business practices with a regularity they naturally found disturbing, and contesting naval procurement policies that required extraordinary research commitments and product guarantees.

In the final analysis, both parties had to overcome the ancient ambivalence that traditionally exists between buyer and seller. Although this situation would never disappear, the Navy and industry managed to identify and reconcile contending motives, goals, and expectations in the process of composing solutions to their often paralyzing confrontations. In this way, by 1940, early incompatibility gave way to a greater degree of cooperation and a mature command technology for submarines.

For the United States Navy this process of evolution began with the Great War. The success of the German U-boat in that conflict served as the catalyst for a closer examination of the submarine's potential, making the Navy's future relationship with the submarine industry a critical factor in addressing the most fundamental questions of strategy, design, and engineering during the twenty-six years between 1914 and 1940.

During this time the Navy and industry came to appreciate the degree of their mutual dependence. Close cooperation was essential if the Navy and its contractors wanted to develop the best vessel while insuring healthy prosperity in the private sector. The technical conflicts and stark budgetary realities of the postwar years reinforced this fact. Traditional business practices and attitudes, however, often posed the greatest obstacle to these goals. Although companies like Electric Boat Company of Groton, Connecticut, the Navy's premier submarine contractor, had become increasingly responsive before the war to naval needs, they initially recoiled at the implications of a true command technology. Businessmen like Henry Carse, Electric Boat's president, wanted to cooperate with the Navy, but not to the extent that the association would endanger the company's hold on the market by depriving it of the initiative for setting policy, prices, and research and development priorities.

Many leading naval officers held a sharply contrasting point of view. They did not regard building warships as routine business, and refused to be treated as ordinary customers. Instead they demanded long-range commitments from industry and a degree of naval control over quality and price that went far beyond the usual relationship between buyer and seller.

Indeed, Rear Admiral Robert S. Griffin, Chief of the Bureau of Engineering (BUENG) from 1913 to 1921, felt that the Navy had to supply strong leadership if it hoped to guide the naval-industrial partnership.[4] If industry assumed this role, he reasoned, market variations and the profit motive could become the dominant factor in submarine development. In this environment, providing for the Navy's domestic needs might only become a matter of supply

3

and demand or even monopoly. Defining missions and roles for the Navy and industry became another vital part of the debate.

Any study of the Navy's relationship with industry in the construction of the American submarine fleet must address a number of key questions: Were the Navy's "technical bureaus"—Bureau of Engineering, Bureau of Construction and Repair, and Bureau of Ordnance—and the American shipbuilding industry able to design and build an effective vessel, one that could compare favorably with the German U-boat? Were the boats built in the United States before Pearl Harbor durable and reliable over the long run? Did the hull design, surface and submerged dynamics, armament, optics, and, most important of all, propulsion, reflect a satisfactory degree of expertise on the part of the Navy and the private sector?

Furthermore, to what extent did private industry and the U.S. Navy cooperate in the design and development of the vessels making up the submarine fleet? Was there a high degree of teamwork or an adversarial relationship between the Navy and leading American submarine contractors like Electric Boat and the Lake Torpedo Boat Company?

The topical organization of this study will allow the reader to focus uninterrupted on these major issues affecting submarine construction and the naval-industrial relationship. Chapter One sets the stage by examining submarine design and development, the industrial base and available technology in America, and the management of contracts and construction during the 1890–1916 period. Chapter Two investigates the naval debate over what types of submarines to build, highlighting the major issues and personalities influencing the resolution of that debate. Chapter Three offers an analysis of the Navy's industrial base for submarine construction during the period 1916–1940, paying particular attention to the policies and capabilities of the Electric Boat Company and the Lake Torpedo Boat Company. The balance of the work then investigates the major challenges, such as optics, habitability, weaponry, and propulsion, encountered by both the public and private sectors. The conclusion presents a synthesis, addressing the entire period and the major themes and important figures of naval-industrial relations between 1914 and 1940.

American shipbuilding talent and technology in this period, taking its cue from the Navy's expectations of the submarine and the ability of the bureaus to channel and manage private and public resources, laid the foundation for the capability and quality of modern submarines. It is hoped that this study will promote additional scholarship and historical debate on the nature of the naval-industrial relationship in the United States.

1

Points of Departure, 1880–1916

In the years before the Great War, the American submarine construction industry had a limited capability. The most obvious deficiency lay with the lack of construction facilities. Only two firms in the United States, both in Connecticut, were capable of producing submarines. They were Lake Torpedo Boat Company of Bridgeport and Electric Boat Company (EB) of Groton. The Navy's best shipyards, at Portsmouth, New Hampshire, and Mare Island, California, served the prewar submarine fleet only as repair and overhaul centers.[1]

The submarine was the product of particularly able inventors like John P. Holland and Simon Lake who sought to sell the new vessel to the Navy. Technological development was largely the concern of the private sector, and the Navy Department chose the best finished product from the selection available on the market. Thus the relationship between private submarine builders and the Navy before 1914 was essentially that of vendor and customer in the classic sense.

Indeed, with the exception of France, very few of the world's major naval powers actually committed vital national resources to submarine research and development before the Great War. This function fell to the independent inventors, like Lake and Holland, and private companies such as Vickers of Barrow-Furness, England, and Friedrich A. Krupp A. G. of Essen, which built almost all of Imperial Germany's submarines at Germania Shipyard in Kiel. They were willing to make a long-range investment in research and construction facilities in the hope of dominating the prospective market and setting the pace in technological development. Thus at the beginning of the Great War the United States Navy was not alone in its dependence upon private industry for new submarine designs, state-of-the-art technology, and future construction.

Early Submarine Development

Many officers within the U.S. Navy questioned the value of building submarines. This attitude, common among all of the major Western naval powers during this period, did not precipitate a rejection of the vessel, but rather passive resistance within the officer corps to the new style of warfare made possible by submergence.

This opposition manifested itself in two ways. Some officers simply denied the significance of the submarine. Since it could not achieve the speed and firepower of the battleship, they relegated the submarine to minor support or coastal defense roles and questioned the wisdom of building the vessel in large numbers. Others within the naval service tried to force the submarine into the traditional context of surface fleet strategy and operations. Both of these viewpoints reflected a natural reaction to the potential revolution in maritime conflict suggested by the advent of undersea warfare.

In Holland's original vision the submarine was designed to exploit subsurface operations as its natural environment. For the most part the navies of the world viewed the submarine, not as Holland did, but as a surface vessel occasionally capable of submerged operations. While technically true, this thinking also caused many of the world's naval leaders, like Admiral Alfred von Tirpitz of Germany, to evaluate the submarine's potential purely in terms of its value as an auxiliary to the battle fleet. The revolutionary potential of its capability to submerge was not fully explored or even partially appreciated.

In discussing similar reactions to innovations in naval ordnance technology in his *Men, Machines, and Modern Times*, historian Elting Morison addressed this phenomenon:

> The opposition [to significant innovation], where it occurs, of the soldier and the sailor to such change springs from the normal human instinct to protect oneself, and more especially, one's way of life. . . . Think of it this way. Since the time that the memory of man runneth not to the contrary, the naval society has been built upon the surface vessel. Daily routines, habits of mind, social organization, physical accommodations, conventions, rituals, spiritual allegiances have been conditioned by the essential fact of the ship. What then happens to your society if the ship is displaced . . . by such a radically different weapon as the plane?[2]

What if the radically different weapon was the submarine?

The U.S. Navy's occasionally reluctant involvement with this type of vessel dates from 1888 when the Bureau of Construction and Repair (BUC&R) sponsored a design competition that brought John Holland a naval contract to build *Plunger*. This submarine, powered by steam on the surface and electricity while submerged, displaced 149 tons. It employed control surfaces, or diving planes, to drive it below the surface, while maintaining a small degree of reserve buoyancy.[3] Unfortunately the vessel never performed as expected and Holland eventually returned the contract advances.

Nonetheless, international curiosity in the submarine persisted. By the turn of the century prominent American naval leaders like Admiral George Dewey began calling the submarine a real threat to international surface forces. In this environment the Navy Department decided to acquire its first submarine in 1900. Overcoming competition from fellow American inventor and creator of *Argonaut I*, Simon Lake, Holland sold his newest model, *Holland VI*, to the Navy for $160,000 on 11 April. This 64-ton submarine, commissioned as USS *Holland*, or SS–1, on 12 October of the same year, was equipped with an Otto-type gasoline engine for surface running and electric motors for submerged operations.[4]

Submarine inventor
John P. Holland.
Illustrator unknown.

NH 82899–KN

Over the next three years the Navy acquired six more submarines of this type, known as the A class. These vessels performed harbor defense functions. They could patrol on the surface at 8 knots, losing only 1 knot of this maximum speed after submerging.

On the international scene, designs by Holland, Lake, and European innovators dominated the field. Lake's *Protector*-class submarines appeared in the Russian Imperial Navy before the Great War, while Holland designs served the Japanese and also joined the Royal Navy. The British already had five commissioned Holland boats for coastal defense service by 1903, the same year the U.S. Navy commissioned the seventh and last boat of the A class. Thereafter most of the Royal Navy's submarines were built to Admiralty designs by the Vickers Company.

The Krupp-Germania Shipyard in Kiel became the prime submarine designer and builder for the Kaiser's navy. The Imperial German Navy involved itself in a marginal research and development program at the Imperial Naval Shipyard in Danzig only because Admiral von Tirpitz was less than enthusiastic about this type of vessel. Hence the German navy did not challenge Krupp's lead.

The effort at Krupp-Germania benefitted from both domestic and international design and engineering talent. The Spanish submarine expert

7

NH 53456

The Navy's first submarine, the 64-ton *Holland* (SS–1), was purchased from John Holland in 1900 and commissioned in October of the same year.

Raymondo Lorenzo d'Equevilley-Montjustin, a long-time colleague of the French submarine designer Maxime Laubeuf, and the German engineer Hans Techel contributed their skills to the development of the German U-boats. The former worked at the Krupp-Germania Shipyard at the turn of the century, the latter during the First World War. D'Equevilley's talents led to the construction of Germany's first modern research submarine, *Forelle*. In spite of these advances, Admiral von Tirpitz waited until 1906 to acquire Imperial Germany's first commissioned submarine, the U–1. Krupp-Germania built the boat, which displaced roughly 238 tons and had a design surface speed of 10.8 knots.

In France the strategy of the *Jeune Ecole*, or Young School, emphasized the importance of threatening the commercial sea lanes and the merchant traffic vital to an adversary's economic survival. This strategic perspective welcomed the submarine and provided a very hospitable environment for the early development of submarine technology.[5] Gustav Zédé designed and built the electrically powered *Gymnote* in 1888, and in 1892 participated in the creation of a larger version of this vessel bearing his name.

During this period French submarine technology surpassed all others when Laubeuf created the steam-driven *Narval* in 1899 and then the revolutionary diesel-powered *Aigrette* in 1900. Rudolf Diesel's 1892 invention proved safer to operate than a gasoline engine, especially in the confined atmosphere of a submarine. American designs did not imitate the *Aigrette* until 1909, when the Electric Boat Company began building the F class (SS–20 through 23) at Union Iron Works in San Francisco. These were 330-ton boats with a designed surface speed of 13.5 knots. The New London Ship and Engine Company (Nelseco), an Electric Boat subsidiary, manufactured the diesels for this class.[6]

Combining the influence of the French diesel propulsion with the designs of Holland and Lake, the U.S. Navy's submarines took on a familiar configuration from 1909 through American entry into the Great War. Submarines of the E, H, K, L, M, N, O, and R classes ranged in displacement from 287 to 510 tons, with the fastest boats displaying a top surface speed of barely 14 knots on diesel power.

The U.S. Navy separated these submarines into two groups according to mission. Submarines of the N and O classes, as well as some of the E boats, patrolled American coasts and harbors following a defensive strategy. Even after American entry into the war, these vessels only occasionally ventured out into the western Atlantic in pursuit of the few German U-boats, like the minelayer, U–117, which threatened the North American continent.[7]

Other submarines drew assignments that sent them to hostile European

Courtesy of the Submarine Force Library and Museum, Groton, CT.

NH 92862

The German U-117 minelayer, which approached a surface displacement of 1200 tons, had the range to reach North America. She surrendered to the Allies in November 1918.

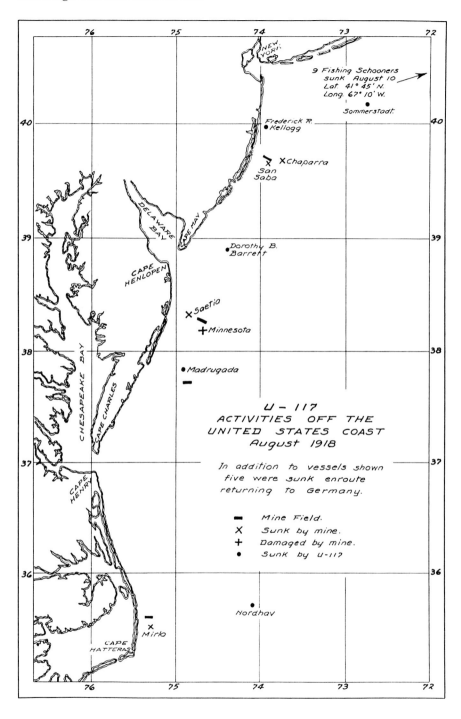

waters after American entry. Some K-, L-, O-, and E-class boats conducted offensive, open-sea operations from the Azores and Bantry Bay in Ireland.[8] They supported the Allied effort to maintain open sea lanes along the European coast and in the approaches to the British Isles.

The offensive mission assigned the submarine force was beyond the capability of its vessels. The submarines assigned to the European theater could not meet the demands of blue water operations. Although the U–117 approached 1200 tons in displacement and could endure protracted sea patrols, none of the American boats exceeded 600 tons. In their eagerness to match the Germans, the American naval leadership tried to use submarines best suited for coastal defense in a strategic and operational context for which they were ill suited.

The Navy Department's plans for these vessels reflected the prevailing surface warfare thinking, which perceived the submarine as a type of destroyer or torpedo boat that should operate with the battle fleet. Thus the first foray into submarine design by the Bureau of Construction and Repair and the Bureau of Steam Engineering produced the faster 15-knot, 800-ton, S-class submarine in 1916 with the assistance of Electric Boat Company and Lake Torpedo Boat Company. This class not only surpassed the best speed of its predecessors by nearly 2 knots, but also increased the submarine's size by at least 300 tons. At virtually the same time, Electric Boat received a commission to design the three boats of the 20-knot T, or AA class, with a normal displacement of 1107 tons. On paper these characteristics, adopted during the First World War, brought the Navy one step closer to having a submarine that could operate with the battle fleet.

Both designs emerged at the start of a period of debate and reevaluation within the American submarine community sparked by the course of the European war and the performance of the German U-boats. During the interwar years, the T- and the S-class boats helped the Navy determine the state of American design and construction capability as well as the strategic role of submarines in future conflicts. In the process these vessels underwent a wide variety of trials and operational demands that their designers never envisioned.

Industrial Base and Available Technology

Although it ostensibly shared the submarine market with the Lake Torpedo Boat Company, Electric Boat actually dominated the industry. In the lean years, before America began to anticipate its involvement in the First World War, the company had lobbied hard on Capitol Hill. By 1914 it had built or contracted for the overwhelming majority of the Navy's submarines. According to Naval Constructor and later Vice Admiral Emory S. Land, "In fact, if you look up history, you'll find that the Navy Department frequently didn't ask for submarines, but they were put in the bill anyway, due to political pressure from this organization."[9]

Electric Boat's political aggressiveness and near-monopoly won the company more enemies than friends in the Navy. By pushing its product into congressional appropriations legislation, it essentially assumed the role of both market leader and naval policymaker. Electric Boat successfully lobbied for the appropriations, designed the vessels, and then proceeded to build its own designs.[10] In this way EB supplied the Navy with two-thirds of all the submarines purchased between 1900 and 1940. When the company's smoothly choreographed relationship with the Navy occasionally came into question, BUENG noted that Electric Boat's "opposing argument intimated, if not expressed, . . . that knowledge of submarine construction was the peculiar property of the Electric Boat Company and that Naval Officers could not hope to produce better solutions of the mystery than those who made it the subject of such intense study as had the officials of that company."[11]

As America prepared for possible involvement in the war, the relationship between the Navy and EB better defined itself over the contracts for the T-class "fleet" submarines.[12] On 2 March 1915 the Navy Department authorized the construction of two of these boats based on its experience developing *Schley*, T–1. The most significant feature of these vessels lay in the General Board's requirement that they reach a surface speed of at least 20 knots to keep pace with the fleet. Initially the Bureau of Construction and Repair issued its own design and called for bids. But neither Lake nor Electric Boat seemed interested in working with Navy designs. They had their own boats on the drawing board and were determined to sell them rather than work with an outside plan. Thus the Navy received no first-class bids from either firm.[13]

Instead each contractor submitted bids based on its own designs and patented systems, without regard for the appropriations limit of $1.5 million set by Congress. Lake offered bids of $1.689 million and $1.748 million for submarines designed to reach 20 knots on the surface; by contract agreement the Navy would have to accept them if they reached 18 knots during trials. The company declared itself ready to build one and would allow the Navy to construct the other at Portsmouth according to company designs.

Electric Boat submitted a bid for two boats or none. Unlike Lake, the EB proposals did not exceed appropriations, but did place BUC&R in an awkward position. EB design 63-B would cost the Navy $1.491 million; if the 63-C proved preferable, the company would ask $1.494 million. Although the bid guaranteed 20 knots, it stipulated high penalty fees for delaying acceptance after trials and construction times of 31 and 33 months respectively. For vessels that essentially copied the design of the T–1, the delivery dates seemed unreasonably distant. Electric Boat also insisted upon a provision in the contract automatically granting an extension of the delivery date equal to the time lost due to late consignments from vital subcontractors. The Navy already had a liberal extension policy that allowed the Secretary of the Navy to grant, at his discretion, extra time to companies beyond the contract limits. The technical bureaus feared that EB's provision would eliminate contract deadlines entirely.

In the end the Navy Department compromised and awarded EB the contract because the company's control over the submarine market left the Navy little choice. By June 1916 EB agreed to accommodate the Navy's request to reduce construction time for the preferred 63–C design from 31 and 33 months to 24 and 26 months for the two remaining T-class fleet boats. The price remained $1.494 million, but the Secretary of the Navy authorized a $20,000 penalty for each knot below 20 if the vessel failed to reach the contract speed during trials. Both parties agreed that the Navy could reject the vessel entirely if it failed to reach a surface speed of at least 19 knots.

Although the Navy and EB reached an agreement that helped get construction underway, the Navy came away from the experience more convinced than ever that the company intended to keep a tight hold on submarine design and production. The contract reflected only EB's technology and showed few signs of Navy influence. The vessels were a company design powered by EB's Nelseco engines. Beyond determining the essential characteristics for the boats through the General Board, EB limited the impact of the Navy's influence to the reduction in the projected construction time.

As the only other firm in the business, Lake Torpedo Boat Company was caught between the power of Electric Boat and the inclination of BUC&R to develop Portsmouth as an alternative to the private sector. In spite of this precarious position, the company produced some of the best and most reliable of the Navy's submarines. Financial and management difficulties, however, plagued the company during the prewar years. These problems prevented it from finishing the G–1 through 3.[14] However, using improved management methods and designs, the company did build the L–5 through 7 between 1914 and 1916. These vessels joined the fleet in time to serve during the First World War.[15]

One factor that would determine the private firm's ability to develop and construct submarines for the Navy was funding. Without adequate congressional support, the legislative appropriations to develop the submarines of the future and the resources to finance regular construction would never materialize. Unfortunately this political facet of the problem reflected, as one might expect, a general and international lack of interest in submarines among ranking officers professionally reared on board surface vessels. If the Navy's leadership preferred to disregard the submarine, how could the submariners expect Congress to provide needed money and attention?

Experienced submarine officers, such as then-Lieutenant Land (CC), felt that responsibility for these conditions lay with the Navy Department and its policies on ship priorities and construction.[16] With a more concerted effort on the part of the department, the Navy could improve the political environment and arouse the national leadership to effective action. As matters now stood, officers with practical experience and engineering expertise would not spend their careers with a novice submarine service suffering from a shortage of trained personnel, low on the Navy's list of priorities, and possessing neither its own training school nor any immediate prospect of improvement. Furthermore, the complex and intricate nature of the submarine and the lack of skilled technical officers made the engineering difficulties acute. A vessel of this sort required parts and systems that would work smoothly and with great dependability.[17]

Before American entry into the First World War the primitive Navy submarine program lacked something as basic as a reliable diesel engine for surface running, and the prospects for overcoming this problem were not bright. Both the Crescent Shipyard of Elizabethport, New Jersey, and Electric Boat outfitted the Navy's earliest submarines with gasoline internal combustion engines.[18] The volatility of gasoline always made it a dangerous product to handle and store in a confined space. Not surprisingly, within a year of Rudolf Diesel's introduction of a new technology in his 1892 paper, "Theory and Construction of a Rational Heat Engine," machinery manufacturers in Europe and America rushed to obtain licenses to manufacture the new diesel engine. Obviously the submarine was only one of many possible applications for the diesel engine, but this technology particularly suited the needs of undersea warfare. Diesel oil proved far less dangerous than gasoline to use and store. Furthermore, this engine employed the heat created by intense pressure to effect combustion rather than the potentially dangerous sparkplug.

In 1893 the earliest licenses to build engines according to Diesel's specifications went to his initial financial and industrial supporters, Maschinenfabrik-Augsburg A. G. and Friedrich Krupp.[19] Four years later this technology came to the United States when Adolphus Busch of St. Louis acquired the American rights to produce diesels. He intended to act as a licensing agent, selling the manufacturing rights to individual subcontractors as the demand for this type of machinery increased.

In 1911, when these efforts proved unprofitable, the Busch Company entered into an agreement with Sulzer Brothers, Ltd., of Switzerland, another diesel patent holder. Through this arrangement, Busch was to blend his manufacturing and marketing experience in America with the engineering expertise of the Sulzer firm. By 1913 the Busch-Sulzer Brothers Diesel Engine Company had produced its own version of Diesel's engine for the American market.[20]

14

From 1900 to 1934 Busch-Sulzer's only major rival for submarine diesel contracts was Electric Boat. After obtaining a license from Sulzer's European rival, Maschinenfabrik Augsburg-Nürnberg (MAN), Electric Boat subcontracted with the Fore River Shipbuilding Company to build the first twelve diesels used in American submarines.[21] These engines powered the four F-class and two E-class boats that became the first diesel-powered submarines in the Navy.

Finding the facilities at Quincy inadequate, Electric Boat transferred its diesel works to Groton, just across the Thames River from New London, Connecticut. Frank Cable, who joined EB in 1901 after driving the experimental vessels built by John Holland, selected the site for the new diesel facility. Plant construction began in 1910, and in the following year Nelseco began functioning as an independently operated subsidiary of EB.

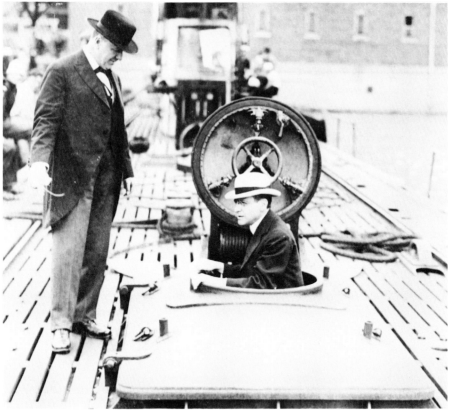

NH 56905

Secretary of the Navy Josephus Daniels (left) and Secretary of War Newton D. Baker inspect the captured German U–117.

15

The diesels for the E and F-class submarines, begun at Quincy, were finished at the new Nelseco Groton facility.[22]

From the beginning BUENG allowed Busch-Sulzer and Nelseco to claim the construction of submarine diesel engines as their own private domain. This was the consequence of a Navy Department policy permitting the primary contractors to determine who would supply the propulsion machinery for the submarines they built for the fleet. Thus on the eve of American entry into the Great War, it had become accepted practice that all machinery for EB vessels would come from Nelseco. At the same time Busch-Sulzer signed an exclusive contract to supply the Lake Torpedo Boat Company.

Concerned about the state of American industrial preparedness for war, congressional leaders initiated debate on the hotly contested Naval Act of 29 August 1916.[23] This measure, which authorized a continuous construction program of 156 ships, had characteristics that profoundly disturbed many in Congress. Many opponents believed the act unfairly bound future Congresses to the program, seemed to make involvement in European affairs inevitable, gave the military far too much power, and drew America into the armaments race as a serious participant.

This piece of legislation also created the Council of National Defense, which took stock of domestic industrial capability to wage war and allowed the Navy to begin building ships and submarines in much greater numbers.[24] Congress specifically included a provision in the bill for the construction of thirty new submarines. Approximately one month before the declaration of war against Germany, the Appropriations Act of 4 March 1917 reinforced the August legislation by adding eighteen more boats to the submarine construction program, while the Navy used resources from the Naval Emergency Fund for twenty more.[25]

With the availability of funds for new construction, the Navy leadership addressed some basic problems neglected earlier because of the submarine's low priority. Procedures as fundamental as the proper administrative plan for formulating approved submarine designs now came down the chain of command from the desk of Secretary of the Navy Josephus Daniels. He decreed that the Navy Department, specifically the General Board, should establish the characteristics of the vessel, while the Bureaus of Construction and Repair and Steam Engineering should address the physical problems of incorporating these attributes in a restricted space.[26] The Chief of Naval Operations (CNO), a position created in 1915 and charged with general responsibility for fleet readiness, had the authority to draft a final comment on ship characteristics before the General Board's recommendations went to the secretary.[27] He did not, however, have authority over the bureaus.

For their part, American submarine designers, engineers, and operators knew well the strategic, technical, and production demands before them. The terrible shortage of experienced officers to assist the General Board and to serve as division commanders or construction inspectors undermined the Navy's ability to build and increased its admiration for British and German accomplishments. The latter had suitable tenders and bases, standardized types, specialized features adopted freely without patent restrictions in wartime, and the flexibility to adopt new technology, given the opportunity.

The British made a commitment to the submarine much earlier than Americans did, providing officers of command rank to organize and direct their effort while American naval leaders still debated the nature of the weapon, and experienced officers in the fleet preferred the glory and challenge of surface duty. The British also seemed far less haphazard in their approach to development. They collected data from thoroughly tested prototypes, which helped standardize the vessels built by their contractors.[28]

The U.S. Navy also needed a rational, well-planned approach to developing operational submarine designs and then efficiently executing the designs at the best facilities. However, chronic lack of technical support personnel along with inadequate facilities for training, berthing, and storage led Lieutenant Commander Guy W. Castle of the Bureau of Steam Engineering to admit that "we cannot claim to have attained either in organization or material development, an efficiency equal to that of the two leaders—Britain and Germany."[29]

As America entered the First World War, the absence of a central authority to coordinate the expertise of the Navy and private industry quickly handicapped the construction program. Although the Navy had ninety-six boats under construction at the Portsmouth Naval Shipyard and five other private facilities by 30 November 1917, none of the contractors seemed capable of keeping pace with demand. The General Board complained to the Secretary of the Navy that, although submarines were second only to destroyers in construction priority, the yards could not maintain their schedules. Emory Land suggested that the shortage of skilled labor at the yards and the lack of money to sustain the pace of construction reflected the Navy Department's less-than-precise estimation of the submarine fleet's needs in the conflict.[30]

With the many imperatives surrounding mobilization, the Navy Department had a difficult time consistently defining and maintaining the relative priority of the submarine in the wartime construction program. In the autumn of 1918 an Emergency Fleet Corporation note received by Union Iron Works, EB's primary West Coast subcontractor, did not place submarines high on the list of naval construction priorities; destroyers and battleships whose keels were already laid and Emergency Fleet Corporation merchant vessels merited higher priority.

This viewpoint, if unchallenged, would have denied vital material and labor resources to Union Iron Works and other submarine construction facilities.

Electric Boat protested against this ranking as well as the tenth-place priority allocated to submarines in a Navy Department communication to Commander D. C. Nutting (CC), the Navy's supervising constructor at Union Iron Works. In response Daniels clarified the issue by admitting that the Navy was giving precedence to destroyers, but assured submarine contractors that, in the allocation of resources, their boats would have a much higher rank than the merchant vessels of the Emergency Fleet Corporation.[31]

In spite of this confusion over priorities, the Navy promptly proceeded to build boats of the L, O, R, and T classes.[32] The appropriations bill had funded the twenty-seven boats of the R class. The Secretary of the Navy authorized cash premiums for each vessel of the O class completed early by the contractor. For the O–3 through 10 series the contract provided a bonus of one-tenth of 1 percent, or $548 per day. Daniels hoped that this approach would provide the private sector with greater motivation to finish before the contract deadline. The first of the 1107-ton class designed to accompany the fleet, *Schley*, or T–1, carried the same premium offer, which amounted to $1,350 for each day saved. The BUC&R limited the total premiums available for any single submarine to 20 percent. This was later increased to 30 percent on the

NH 42535

This aerial view of Union Iron Works, Electric Boat's major West Coast subcontractor for submarine construction, shows four submarines in drydock during the First World War.

NH 44557

O–11 is fitted out at the Lake Torpedo Boat Company, Bridgeport, Connecticut, summer 1918.

first truly mass-produced series of American submarines, the S class.[33]

The techniques used by the Navy to speed construction went well beyond premiums. The Navy Department authorized the Board of Inspection and Survey to conduct a curtailed trial schedule on new submarines to rush them into the six-month and ten-day trial period prescribed by the contract. This practice would offer the operating forces an opportunity to gain valuable experience with the vessel before final trials. The normally intricate trial schedule was consolidated into eight tests. The board had to conduct the four-hour, full-power main engine trial; the one-hour submerged trial at full speed; the steering gear, hand pump, depth; and three-hour battery tests, as well as the windlass test and the firing of a single dummy torpedo from each tube.[34]

The war made it imperative for the Navy to build as many functional submarines as possible in the shortest time. A few months before American entry into the war, Assistant Secretary of the Navy Franklin D. Roosevelt had authorized the BUENG to allow the Inspector of Machinery at Groton to approve plans and material delivery schedules for the T–2 and T–3.[35] He made it clear that the acceleration of construction in anticipation of war served the national interest.

Roosevelt may have served the national interest in ways he did not anticipate. With the threat of war and the onset of mobilization, the United States tried to acquire as many capable submarines as possible, pushing aside serious questions of safety and design. This rush to increase the number of boats only served to point up the major weaknesses in the American vessels. Operational submariners and their superiors soon began to question the safety, reliability, and overall capability of these vessels. Of all the boats under construction, only the three T-class fleet submarines represented an effort to exploit the unique features of the submarine. Nowhere could one find a consensus on the most favorable submarine design, the strategy for which existing American submarines were well suited, or cogent plans for meeting labor and material needs for future construction.[36]

Increasing the size of the submarine force highlighted the fact that vessels were not up to standard, but neither the Navy nor private industry had satisfactory alternatives. Thus the Navy found itself building many types that were seriously outdated, with the most appropriate designs and tasks for future American submarines remaining unclear.

Contracts: Specifications and Administration

Until the Bureaus of Construction and Repair and Steam Engineering collaborated on the design of the S-class submarines in 1915 and 1916, they relied completely on the private sector for designs, advanced technology, and construction.[37] Electric Boat and Lake produced plans that followed or approximated the requirements set by the General Board. These firms and their subcontractors did the required engineering, calculations, and engine selection and produced a complete set of specifications, as well as preliminary and contract designs.[38]

The preliminary design constituted the first concrete proposal of a new design by a private firm to the bureaus, the General Board, and the Secretary of the Navy. At this point the design had progressed from concept to full-fledged plan, complete with detailed specifications. After naval authorities approved the design and suggested necessary alterations, the originating firm drew up the contract design.

During this period the Navy confined itself to contract administration and supervisory services. Although the bureaus negotiated agreements independently with specific companies, the Office of the Judge Advocate General (JAG) conducted the bidding and approved the contract's legal content and form. The Bureau of Supplies and Accounts (BUSANDA) then took responsibility for payment as ship construction progressed or after the delivery of materials, parts, or systems. Beginning in 1917 the Navy Compensation Board, in conjunction with BUSANDA, determined the allowable costs specified in each contract.[39]

The Navy Department used two basic types of contracts to govern these agreements with industry. A fixed-price contract determined the cost of the construction project at the outset and the amount of profit the contractor would realize. Used before and during the war, this instrument emerged as the contract form most preferred by the Navy during the postwar period. The cost-plus-percentage-of-cost type of contract allowed the purveyor to realize, as profit, a percentage of the total cost incurred for production. Because the contractor's profits rose at the same rate as his costs, the private vendor had no incentive to keep costs down. The Navy Department discontinued this type of contract after the war because it encouraged profiteering. After 1918 the Navy Department used the cost-plus-fixed-fee type instead, which specified profits in dollar amounts, regardless of cost.

Once the contract agreement went into effect, BUC&R and BUENG applied the same system of on-site supervision at the shipyards and factories for submarines as they did for surface ships. A naval Supervisor of Shipbuilding (SUPSHIPS) and his staff of inspectors and engineers took up residence at each shipyard. They reported to BUC&R on the progress of construction, as well as on weight and cost changes at variance with the contract design. As the on-site representative of BUC&R and BUENG, the SUPSHIPS's office also approved or disapproved any design changes suggested by the vendor. The bureaus also provided a corps of resident and itinerant purchasing inspectors of both naval machinery and naval materials who supervised the production of related parts and systems at a host of subcontractor plants all over the country. In this way the bureaus tried to insure that the shipyards built sound vessels and subcontractors delivered systems that met naval specifications and standards. BUENG assigned the inspectors of naval machinery, and the BUC&R appointed the inspectors of naval material.

With the advent of the U-boat threat, the technical bureaus went beyond administration and supervision to seek a greater role in the design and construction of submarines. Although the methods of supervision remained the same, the Navy now became a full partner with the private sector in the development of submarines. BUC&R and BUENG generated proposals and provided the engineering and mathematical expertise to transform them into preliminary designs. The bureaus then sought the opinion of the CNO and the General Board before refining approved preliminary plans and specifications into contract designs. These designs formed the basis of awards to the Portsmouth Naval Shipyard, Mare Island Naval Shipyard, or one of the private firms.

Electric Boat and Lake employed the same process in developing new plans, but now had to compete with the Navy bureaus to determine which designs would eventually join the fleet. This development occurred for the first time during the competition to determine the best plans for the S class in 1916.[40]

A naval shipyard, although burdened with the same construction responsibilities as Electric Boat or Lake, benefitted substantially from its direct relationship with the Navy. The private sector still needed to go through the bidding-award process involving JAG, BUSANDA, and the Compensation Board, but the Navy, of course, had fewer administrative obstacles to overcome at its own bureaus and yards. Conflicts involving contract responsibilities, cost and weight variations, or design changes during construction presented less formidable obstacles when the bureaus worked internally with a shipyard under direct Navy control. Furthermore, naval facilities like Portsmouth did not have to pay taxes or worry about cash flow, bank loans, or capital costs. Thus, by developing a design and construction capability at the Portsmouth Naval Shipyard during the interwar years, BUC&R helped keep costs under control and provided EB and Lake with an able competitor.

2

Questions of Strategy and Design

One of my classmates was in command of a submarine, one of the D-boats, and when he went aboard the Flagship at Newport one summer, the Commander-in-Chief said, "Why, hello, Mr. Bingham, when are you going to get back in the Navy?"

—Vice Admiral Emory S. Land,
speaking about the period before the Great War.

One factor that hindered the effectiveness of the naval-industrial partnership for submarine construction during the 1920s was the Navy's inability to determine the ideal strategy for the wartime employment of its submarines. This resulted from the gradual recognition by naval authorities that American submarine technology, in a primitive state during and after the Great War, would not support previous assumptions about the proper role for the submarine. A sobering postwar comparison of American submarines with the German U-boats precipitated a design and strategy debate that led to a complete redefinition of the submarine's place in a future war after 1928.

In 1919 American naval planners had not yet developed a submarine strategy predicated upon the unique capabilities of this type of warship. Drawing on lessons offered by the Great War, Naval War College problems during the 1920s called for the submarine to operate by divisions or sections, usually in direct support of the fleet, and discouraged individual submarine offensive efforts unless an exceptional opportunity presented itself. The submarine's mission was to serve the surface fleet by locating enemy supply lines, gathering intelligence, and disrupting communications. American naval analysts rejected the idea of a war against commerce, similar to the strategy employed by the Germans during the First World War, as distasteful. This left scouting, harbor defense, and mine laying as the only honorable options. A primarily offensive role against enemy warships or merchant vessels, independent of the surface fleet or an impending surface action, was never seriously considered. Thus American strategic thinkers of the early interwar period tethered vessels like the S–1 (SS–105) to the surface fleet if their seakeeping qualities suited the boats for blue-water operations. Otherwise American submarines generally found themselves relegated to coastal defense, their principal prewar mission.[1]

Unfortunately neither the Navy nor American private industry could produce a technically reliable fleet submarine capable of keeping up with a surface force beyond 17 or 18 knots in the best conditions. American technology simply could not equip the Navy's submarines to fulfill the strategic role assigned to them.

Thus, although strategy traditionally determined the characteristics of a ship, the opposite was unexpectedly true for the submarine. The state of American submarine technology made it clear that a strategic accommodation was in order. The Navy Department had to determine a profitable way of using the vessels it had while exploring the most promising future alternatives in design and strategy.

Looking for the Best Design: The Standardization Boards

On the eve of American entry into the Great War the question of the most suitable submarine design to build became a vital and controversial issue.[2] In the summer of 1916, with the encouragement of both Lieutenant Emory Land (CC) and Rear Admiral Albert W. Grant, Commander Submarine Force, Atlantic Fleet, the General Board of the Navy proposed adding to the fleet not only defensive, coastal patrol submarines between 400 and 600 tons like the L, O, and R classes, but also the larger T-class fleet submarines. The T-1 through 3 would have dramatically increased displacement and speed to help them perform the blue-water tasks that the lighter coastal boats would find difficult.

However, a combination of older, smaller vessels and three experimental fleet boats would not provide a potent combination for fighting a war. The Navy needed a standardized type; in this way it could increase production and gain design and construction experience for both the Navy and for the few submarine contractors in the private sector.

Admiral Grant developed this theme in a timely report submitted to the Navy Department on 21 March 1917. He insisted that "the time is now ripe to settle on a policy of Department standard detail design of such features in a submarine which have evolved to a satisfactory state from practical use in the service." The report emphasized the inexperience of those building the submarines, as well as of those officers expected to approve plans and supervise construction. Grant suggested the creation of a submarine board composed of representatives of the technical bureaus and officers with operational experience, so they could combine knowledge of the latest technological advances with a commanding officer's practical viewpoint. Standardization by a committee of this sort would bring quicker production and better performance to both shipbuilding and operations.[3]

In April the Bureau of Ordnance (BUORD), in conjunction with the Bureau of Construction and Repair and the Bureau of Steam Engineering, drew the attention of the Secretary of the Navy to many of Admiral Grant's suggestions. The technical bureaus concluded that the government should assume control of vital patents in wartime, and new designs should benefit from both the ideas of the submarine force commanders and the bureaus.[4] They went on to

Vice Admiral Emory S. Land.

NH 85531

suggest that an unofficial board, comprised of experienced submarine officers and personnel in the Navy bureaus responsible for design and construction, should examine and debate the best characteristics for future submarines.[5]

Many of Grant's suggestions originally came from a letter written to him by Commander Yates Stirling, Jr., commanding officer of Submarine Base, New London. Using the highly centralized British and German administrative models, Stirling had called for a division of submarine affairs commanded by an officer of flag rank with genuine authority and practical knowledge who would, as part of his mission, effect the removal of peacetime patent restrictions on wartime construction and earnestly promote the education of designers, supervising constructors, and operational officers. Grant and Stirling believed the fleet could trust this kind of organization to remain sensitive to operational needs while preserving high technical standards.[6] Then perhaps submarines of a quality comparable to the German U-boat would emerge from American shipyards.

When Secretary of the Navy Josephus Daniels approved the idea and called for the establishment of a Submarine Standardization Board on 20 June 1917, Admiral Grant quickly chose Commander Stirling as the candidate for senior member. The board over which Stirling presided was composed of five individual committees drawn from the Submarine School in New London,

Submarine Divisions 2 and 3, and Submarine Divisions 4, 5, and 6. These five components each proceeded to examine, in some detail, the most important military and human characteristics that would have to fit into the new displacement limit of 800 tons set by the secretary. Since naval authorities had never completely defined the characteristics they desired in a submarine, the committees had to discuss everything from diesel engines and electric motors to ventilation and running lights.

In this way the war forced the United States to ask the most basic questions about its future submarines. In his instructions to the board, Admiral Grant even asked the members to respond to specific questions pertaining to basic characteristics. How fast should a boat move on the surface and submerged? Is 800 tons a sufficient displacement? How many torpedo tubes should each vessel have and how many torpedoes might be needed?

The characteristics that emerged from the board's deliberations not only exceeded the displacement figure set by Daniels but also stretched the limits of American submarine technology. Stirling's people desired a vessel of not less than 1000 tons, with even heavier displacements as soon as technical advances would permit. This boat would move at maximum speeds of 11 knots submerged for two hours and at least 18 knots on the surface for twelve hours. The traditional torpedo tube configuration of four forward and one aft would not change; a complement of eighteen torpedoes was suggested as the most potent and safe main armament. Diving or surfacing, it was pointed out, should take as few as one to as many as eight minutes, and the boat must demonstrate the capability to withstand the ocean's pressure at depths of up to 200 feet.[7]

Technological and financial realities helped shape the reception given to the Stirling report. Of all the suggested attributes of this vessel, the displacement presented the greatest challenge. If a boat displaced 400 or 600 tons, the speeds suggested by the Stirling board were certainly attainable. However, a vessel displacing 1000 tons would place requirements on submarine diesels currently beyond submarine propulsion technology. At the time, the three T-class boats fell into the category of experimental vessels, and their 1107 tons barely exceeded the weight suggested as a standard for the immediate future by the board. Furthermore, the production of the Navy's newest type of submarine, the 800-ton S class, had just begun, and the bureaus wanted to avoid the expense of a major design revision. Consequently the recommendations of the board would have a significant influence on submarine construction and alterations that might be made to the S class, but only within limits precisely defined by accountants and bureau designers.

In October 1917 a newly instituted standardization board met to consider the Stirling recommendations and to establish officially the characteristics for future construction. Chaired by retired Commander John S. Doddridge, it included some of the Navy's better submarine engineers and commanding officers, like Naval Constructor Emory Land and Commander Chester W. Nimitz of Submarine Force, Atlantic Fleet. Nimitz later distinguished himself during the Second World War as Commander in Chief, Pacific Fleet. After four months of deliberation, the general conclusions were predictable. The Doddridge board set aside the Stirling board's 1000-ton displacement figure as suitable only for the experimental T class. Instead the Doddridge board recommended retaining the current 800-ton S-boat alternative, concluding that "no radical departure from the present S-boats should be attempted."

The contributions of the two boards to submarine design provide an interesting contrast. The Stirling board was the first to address the major concerns of the submarine community. In some cases it suggested radical solutions to current needs. Far more conservative in its outlook, the Doddridge board affirmed the wartime decisions of the secretary and the technical bureaus. Its most valuable contribution came in the development of specific design attributes.

What the Stirling group did in general, the Doddridge board did in the particular. The desire to enhance the performance of the crew by improving habitability—that is, the quality of living conditions aboard a submarine—provides a good example.[8] In considering ventilation as a prime factor in determining habitability, the Stirling board wanted to make sure that the engine, motors, and batteries remained at a proper temperature without fouling the air in crew compartments. Thus it raised questions about blowers, air intake openings in the hull, and the temperature and quality of the air in each compartment.

In contrast the Doddridge board studied the fine points of ventilation with an eye toward ensuring greater habitability as well as increased mechanical reliability. It concluded that a powerful centralized ventilation system would serve all four divisions of the submarine—battery, main engine, motor, and crew areas—while limiting the number of induction openings in the hull. They also said that for the safety and comfort of the crew, a standard ventilation system should take no more than ten minutes to renew the air in all parts of the boat.

A further comparison between the two groups' views on diesel engines suitable for submarines illustrates the Doddridge board's charge to set specific research and development priorities within existing displacement and budget restrictions. The Stirling board explored the more promising types of propulsion in a general way, but the Doddridge group focused on systems of proven reliability and practicality that would meet the Navy's needs in the near future. The members drove home the necessity for diesel dependability and insisted on efficient fuel economy. They agreed with the Stirling board on the need for air-starting and -reversing as long as the system remained within reason in terms of size and weight.[9] The sense of urgency induced by the war came through in their demand for standardization, simplicity, and financial support for research and development as part of each congressional appropriations bill. They firmly rejected untried designs as a waste of time and resources.[10]

The Inevitable Comparison: The S class Versus the U-boat

The Doddridge Submarine Standardization Board finished the groundbreaking work of Commander Yates Stirling's group by working out submarine characteristics in much greater and more precise detail within the context of a restricted budget and wartime needs. The S class, as the Doddridge board model for future standardization, helped the Navy come of age in submarine design and development.

Thrust into the limelight as the Navy's ideal type for the immediate postwar years, the fifty vessels of this class placed every possible technological dilemma before the bureaus. Conceived in 1916, before the Stirling and Doddridge boards were convened, and first commissioned in 1919, the S-class design soon showed the technical bureaus the difficulty of achieving their ambitions for this type. From the day they first appeared on the ways at Electric Boat Company, Lake Torpedo Boat Company, and Portsmouth Naval Shipyard, the S class had presented a challenge. The bureaus intended to make this class the best submarines American naval technology could produce. Besides the 800-ton displacement, its most important features were a 21-inch torpedo tube and an emphasis on habitability, engine reliability, silent electric motors, and endurance. A full two-thirds of the crew were to have berth space at any one time, all crewmen were to have lockers and gas masks, and the vessel was to have excellent ventilation, complete with absorbers to retard the accumulation of carbon dioxide in the air. Only tried and tested diesels could provide dependability, serviceability and swift production. The electric motors were to exhibit exceptional workmanship and silent operation. To ensure the best utility, the boat was to carry enough fuel to allow a cruising radius of 6000 miles at 11 knots on the surface.[11]

The S–1 (SS–105) illustrated the fundamental problems suffered by the entire class. Fore River Shipbuilding Company built the S–1 under contract to the Electric Boat Company. In the report of her final trials submitted to the Navy Department by the Board of Inspection and Survey, the list of problems and machinery casualties was demoralizing. The diesel engines, manufactured by Nelseco experienced so many breakdowns that the board suggested a new engine for the vessel. Vibration in the propulsion system caused torsional stresses which cracked cylinders, cylinder heads, castings, and crankshafts.[12]

This situation became a major crisis when the operational forces and the bureaus compared the outstanding quality of the German U-boats captured at the end of the First World War with these S-class submarines. The clear technical superiority of the U-boats rocked the American submarine

S–1 (SS–105), the first of the S class plagued by excessive vibration and breakdowns of its diesel engines.

establishment and initiated a twenty-year debate between the operational forces, the technical bureaus, and the General Board.

In November 1918 under the direction of Rear Admiral Samuel S. Robison, Commander Squadron 3 of the Atlantic Fleet Patrol Force, the Navy began collecting information on the technical quality and performance of the vessels of the Imperial German Navy. For his report compiled for the benefit of the technical bureaus, Robison and his assistant, Captain Arthur J. Hepburn, inspected the latest type of U-boats in each class. The U–164 and U–124 gave Robison experience with standard German patrol submarines, and the UB–148 provided an example of a coastal vessel; the UC–105 submarine minelayer filled out the picture of German U-boat capabilities.[13]

As Robison prepared to file his report, Commander Emory Land anticipated the admiral's findings by two months; he communicated with Secretary Daniels on 4 February 1919 on the importance of gaining first-hand knowledge of the captured German submarines. Land had taken his experience with the Doddridge board with him when he journeyed to England in July 1918 to serve on the staff of Admiral William S. Sims, Commander U.S. Naval Forces in European Waters. He toured the German and Austrian shipyards and learned the details of the examination of the UC–105, UB–149, U–164, and U–124 done in Britain by the officers and crew of the L-class submarines attached to the tender *Bushnell* (AS–2). He strongly suggested that the Navy obtain some of these vessels for close inspection at home.[14]

The submarine force in Europe borrowed these four boats from the British and took them to Portland, England, near Dorset, on 12 December 1918 for almost three weeks. Land could barely avoid superlatives when describing the results of diesel, periscope, and hull tests, as well as the range of which these boats were capable. In the space afforded by this preliminary report to the secretary, Land found it difficult to present a comprehensive picture of all the superior features he and others had discovered in the U-boat. In one flight of admiration and envy he stated, "The diesel engines on these submarines are superior to any other diesel engines in any other submarines in commission in the world." He also lauded German double-hull construction for its resistance to depth charges.[15]

On Land's return from Europe, the General Board summoned him from a new billet at BUC&R and the Submarine Design Board as an expert on the new German technology. Instead of offering direction based upon his broad experience, Land's testimony reflected the confusion created by the sudden realization that the Navy had fallen far behind in submarine technology. To the frustration of Rear Admiral Albert G. Winterhalter and other members of the board, Land did not seem at all sure what a fleet submarine should look like. He admitted that the Chief of Naval Operations had asked him to determine the characteristics of a fleet submarine as part of his mission abroad, but the more he learned the less certain he became. He found "no hard and fast opinion any place as to what the functions of a fleet submarine are," and he took no comfort from the General Board's characteristics, which

Courtesy of Ed Coffer.   NH 100681

The captured U–111, passing an R-class submarine, was a main attraction in the East Coast Victory Bond Tour in mid-1919.

30

projected a surface speed of 25 knots for fleet boats that current diesel technology could not satisfy. With his recently acquired knowledge of the German U-boats, Land knew that the propulsion problem represented only one facet of a comprehensive challenge to the Navy's engineering and design talent.

It seemed that the German experience rewrote the rules of the game just as the Doddridge board arrived at a standard design in the S class. In spite of their cramped conditions and terrible habitability, the U-boats exhibited remarkable reliability, and demonstrated technological superiority. Bringing some of these vessels to the United States became a necessity.[16]

In the spring of 1919 the Navy Department approved the temporary acquisition of six German submarines to allow the technical bureaus and operational forces to take complete advantage of the advances made by their adversary during the war. The U-111 was a standard "Ms," or Mobilization-boat, of approximately the same displacement as the S class.[17] Both the U-117 and the UC-97 were minelayers, the first displacing over 1000 tons in contrast to the latter's 474 tons. The UB-88 and UB-148 performed coastal patrol roles, as opposed to the larger U-140, one of the long-range U-cruisers.

The U-111 and UB-148 underwent tests supervised by the Board of Inspection and Survey; the tests included standardization trials on the surface with varying combinations of engine and electric motor propulsion. The board also conducted submerged trials, torpedo-firing trials, depth tests for hull strength, turning circles, and various tests to evaluate the vessel's submergence and maneuvering capabilities.[18] The Navy's U-boat Plans Committee, which arranged for the transport of the six U-boats from England, specified that these experiments, especially on the U-111, should follow the regimen prescribed by the contract of the American submarine S-2. The outspoken and tenacious Captain Thomas C. Hart, former commander of Submarine Divisions 4 and 5 in European waters and now attached to the CNO's office as an expert on submarine matters, chaired this committee. He and the next senior member, Emory Land, knew all too well the likely outcome of the inevitable comparison with the S class.[19]

The first chance to learn from the U-boats took place on the Atlantic crossing. The opportunity to command the U-111 fell to Lieutenant Commander Freeland A. Daubin, who wrote an extensive report on the vessel's performance. Cast as an effort to supplement the findings of the Board of Inspection and Survey, Daubin's comments confirmed the excellence of the German Ms-boat. The vessel displayed outstanding stability whether at the dock or in the open sea, and responded easily to the controls with a minimum of crew participation. Although the Board of Inspection and Survey reported that it took the U-111 one minute and sixteen seconds to dive, Daubin insisted that his crew had the boat submerged and trimmed in forty seconds. The

Captain Thomas C. Hart, as head of the Submarine Section in the Office of the Chief of Naval Operations, 20 January 1918.

NH 100808

periscope was easily used, and he found the air compressors and entire propulsion system rugged, reliable, and easily accessible for lubrication and repair. With two deck guns and four torpedo tubes forward and two aft for twelve torpedoes, the U–111 offered its commander a potent weapon. The vessel presented a low profile and small freeboard and provided a remarkably smooth ride in foul weather.[20]

The technical bureaus, sharing the intense curiosity and excitement of the operational forces as well as the concern of their own experts, threw themselves into a detailed examination of the U–111 and other German submarines.[21] They wanted to make sure the Navy fully exploited "the features of this vessel which have been shown under operating conditions to be superior to the corresponding features in submarines of our own design."[22]

For BUC&R the active operational condition of the U–111 made this vessel particularly valuable. The Navy could not benefit from a dismantled or stationary boat nearly as much as it could from a seagoing example of the latest in submarine technology.[23] Indeed, the Board of Inspection and Survey made extensive use of the Navy's experience with the U–111 in its preliminary trial of the S–2 (SS–106). The board noted for example that the Busch-Sulzer diesel in the Lake-built S–2 proved far more reliable than the S–1's Nelseco machinery, but exhibited fuel and lubrication oil leaks that did not appear in the MAN diesels of the U–111. In the words of the preliminary trial report:

"In this respect the engine compared unfavorably with the engines on the U–111, recently examined by the board."[24] In spite of later acquisitions the U–111 remained the Navy's primary research and training vessel of all the captured U-boats brought to the United States.[25]

In addition to their use in educating the Navy's operational forces, the German boats were made available to representatives of the most important private contractors in the submarine field. After BUC&R petitioned the Navy Department to allow the representatives of some private firms to examine the U-boats, the Chief of Naval Operations ordered BUC&R and BUENG to compile a list of the firms that could benefit from such an experience. BUC&R's list of ten included Electric Boat and Lake Torpedo Boat as well as subcontractors Kollmorgen (periscopes), Ingersoll Rand (air compressors), and others. The selection submitted by BUENG highlighted propulsion and electrical companies in a list four pages long.[26]

BUENG displayed greater willingness than did BUC&R to profit from the technological advances offered by the U-boats. While the latter debated the positive and negative attributes of German double-hull construction and contented itself with securing diagrams and plans of the designs in question, BUENG ordered the removal of all propulsion and electrical systems from every U-boat save the essential U–111. These electric motors, diesel engines,

Captain Freeland A. Daubin, former commander of the captured U–111.

NH 50685

33

and other parts became part of a cooperative educational process conducted by BUENG with private industry. The bureau even wished to distribute some of the machinery and mechanisms among its vendors for study and improvement. The Wilson administration had no objection to this, but Acting Secretary of the Navy Franklin D. Roosevelt stipulated that no machinery could be given to the private sector. The Navy would retain ownership, allowing firms to use the systems taken from the U-boats for research. [27]

From the beginning BUENG used German submarine technology as a catalyst to spur American industry to refine current designs for propulsion and electrical systems. In the past the bureau's efforts to improve the quality of propulsion technology by simply designing its own machinery in competition with the private sector produced poor returns. This process depended upon the quality of the Navy's technology, which left much to be desired. However, if a new and better technology sponsored by the bureau suddenly appeared on the scene, BUENG "confidently believed that better engines would thus be obtained and that long or indefinite delay in obtaining these engines from a possible private contractor would be avoided."[28] Thus the bureau took intense interest in the German propulsion plants.

The more information they collected about the German submarines, the more the technical bureaus and the operational forces realized the extent to which the United States was lagging. The S class did not incorporate the latest in submarine technology, but this was the best the service could hope for in the near future.

In an August 1920 letter to the CNO's Director of Submarines, Lieutenant Commander Holbrook Gibson, Commander Submarine Repair Division of the Philadelphia Navy Yard, allowed a combination of urgency, anger, concern, and uncertainty to rise to the surface. Gibson "found so many things in the German submarines in design, workmanship, etc., that are so vastly superior to ours that such a report [publicly discussing the quality of the systems taken from the U-boats] would not do any particular good, but might have just the opposite result. . . . And it also must be borne in mind that we are getting our information from boats that are three years old in design."[29]

Captain Thomas Hart also communicated with Secretary Daniels regarding the negative impact of the German advances on the U.S. Navy. Hart felt that Daniels should correct current stories in the public press about the preeminence of American submarines. If the officers and men of the submarine community perceived this viewpoint as official, they might conclude, with a corresponding decline in morale, that "no improvement is to be expected as a result of the hard work done with the ex-German submarines."[30]

With the new postwar technical knowledge, fundamental changes in submarine design and performance had to follow. Could the Navy find the money and achieve the internal consensus to bring them about? The cumulative professional, technological, and emotional effect of German technical superiority and the lamentable state of American submarine development would soon explode into a controversy over the inadequacies of the S class and the future direction of the American submarine program.

The Stirling Letter

The sense of urgency and frustration felt by some naval officers over the condition of the submarine fleet reached a climax in 1921 when Captain Yates Stirling, then Commandant of the Philadelphia Navy Yard, penned a letter to the Secretary of the Navy. In this correspondence Stirling roundly condemned the quality of American submarines and their potential to make a positive contribution to the Navy's mission in a future war. He thought American submarines suffered from a litany of technical problems that rendered them totally unreliable for service. These difficulties ranged from diesel and motor malfunctions to severe periscope vibration, poorly designed air compressors, and inferior ventilation systems. The Navy had to become more deeply involved in the design and construction of these vessels, if only to counter the risk of falling victim to a private sector monopoly. From Stirling's viewpoint the Navy had at its disposal the perfect instruments for modernization in the captured German U-boats. The S class made it clear

Rear Admiral David W. Taylor, Chief of the Bureau of Construction and Repair, 1914–1922. Pen and ink portrait by Harry S. Moskovitz, circa 1922.

NH 95289

35

that the technical bureaus and private industry failed to produce a wartime equivalent to vessels like the U–53, a 700-ton Ms-boat with superior seakeeping qualities. Extensive reconsideration of current designs and perhaps a reevaluation of the Navy's system for administering the submarine program were in order.

The Stirling letter naturally prompted a storm of protest from the technical bureaus and the General Board. Rear Admiral David W. Taylor, Chief of BUC&R, dissected Stirling's note in response to Secretary Daniels's request for an opinion, and pointed out that in most instances Stirling's exposé contradicted matters of record. Taylor assured the Secretary of the Navy that BUC&R had indeed made a careful study of the U-boats and had every intention of incorporating the latest German technology in future designs.[31]

That Taylor's comprehensive response to Stirling did not end the matter illustrates the extent to which the captain's observations struck a chord among the various activities responsible for submarine design and operation. When the General Board called a hearing on Stirling's claims, it turned into a testimonial by the operating forces on the utter inadequacy of the Navy's submarines and provided a gauge of the considerable diversity of opinion on the board and at the technical bureaus.

Before the General Board, Captain Stirling acknowledged that the BUC&R had indeed recorded the specifications of the captured U-boats. But he persisted in his criticisms with selections from reports on the S class that he had solicited from ten of the most experienced submarine officers in the Navy, including Captain Hart and Lieutenant Commanders Daubin and Gibson. After reciting a litany against the S boats, Stirling drove home his central point: the methods historically employed by the Navy to develop submarine designs were responsible for the consistent record of mediocrity and failure. The real problem, it seemed, lay with the bureaus. Hart pointed out that it took far too long to convince the technical bureaus of the need to examine and learn from German wartime developments. The bureaus illustrated just how far removed they were from the cutting edge of submarine technology by the low priority they had initially given to obtaining the U-boats for research in the United States.[32]

The controversy created by Stirling's letter and his testimony before the General Board exposed the gulf between the technical bureaus and the operational submarine forces. The technical bureaus took advantage of the captured U-boats to improve the designs and modify the systems of American submarines. Although BUENG displayed greater flexibility in this regard than did BUC&R, both saw the importance of educating themselves in the latest German technology.

However, the operational officers did not benefit from the bureaus' evaluation of this technology. The technical bureaus excluded these officers from decisions on design and engineering matters. Thus the lamentable condition of the S class and the possibility that the bureaus did not appreciate fully the insights provided by the Germans drove Stirling and the officers who supported him to take action. They feared that a lack of communication between those designing and those manning submarines could retard the Navy's submarine program.[33]

Stirling advanced a solution to this predicament that paralleled the proposal to establish a Bureau of Aeronautics for an equally new form of technology first applied to military purposes during the war. He believed that a Bureau of Submarines would focus command authority, operational experience, available money, and all the technological expertise in a single agency that could then produce the best possible undersea vessel for the Navy. Instead of receiving this kind of direction, submariners currently had to go begging because the Navy Department naturally assumed, to use Stirling's words, "that they are better fitted to dispense it [financial and administrative resources] to the prodigal son than he would be to dispense it himself."[34]

A Bureau of Submarines would overcome the natural reluctance of the other bureaus to abandon or revise a prized creation like the S-class design. Neither would it hesitate to copy all or part of the U–111 and its sister boats if the state of American technology made these measures necessary. The development of a seaworthy submarine to fulfill the mission assigned to it would finally take the highest priority.[35]

The General Board did not enthusiastically embrace Stirling's suggestions in its report to the Secretary of the Navy. It defended the S class as the best design BUC&R could have generated during the war. The members also felt that insights gained from the U-boats could have a positive effect on the future of both the S and V types if implementing some of the findings proved financially feasible. The board attributed the propulsion problems in the S class to unhealthy dependence upon Electric Boat. To deal with the problem, they recommended greater bureau participation in design and development, upgrading facilities on both coasts for repair and overhaul, and creation of a school for all enlisted personnel working with submarines.[36]

Ironically, suggestions for a Bureau of Submarines did not only come from the group around Stirling. In his analysis of the debate caused by the Stirling letter, Rear Admiral Sims, by now President of the Naval War College, suggested in a letter to the General Board that the facts regarding the design and production of submarines for the Navy would "demonstrate the futility of attempting further to improve our submarine service through the agency of our present submarine organization...." Sims thought the Navy had waited too long to involve itself in submarine construction and design. He agreed with Stirling that the technical bureaus too often proved unwilling to depart from accepted designs and that this resulted in a reluctance to learn from other nations or agencies as well as a tendency to keep producing the familiar, regardless of quality. He also voiced his suspicion of the private sector, questioning whether its motives inclined them to change old, well-tested, profitable designs.[37]

Sims's opinions only heightened the intensity of the submarine design debate, which had persisted from the time of the Stirling letter until 1930. The discovery of new German submarine technology at the end of the Great War, combined with the traditional uncertainty regarding the submarine's role, placed the Navy in a quandary it could not readily resolve. This awkward situation displayed the ineffectiveness of the Navy's submarine organization. Contention between the technical bureaus, the General Board, and the operational forces paralyzed the decision-making process and deprived the Navy of both a consensus on strategy and design and a coherent plan for the future.

Reaching Consensus

During the years between 1922 and 1931, the submarine community could do little but debate the various issues essential to design and construction. Without a well-coordinated system of resource management and an accord on mission and design, only time and constant debate could turn diversity into consensus. By dividing the responsibility for submarines, the Navy Department guaranteed that the much needed concordance would be slow in coming. Any consensus would have to please the General Board, the technical bureaus, and the Submarine Officers Conference (SOC), a committee of experienced submariners established in 1926 as an advisory group to the Chief of Naval Operations and the Secretary of the Navy.

Parochialism within the bureaus tended to exacerbate these conditions. For example, BUC&R had primary responsibility for coordinating the suggestions of the operational forces with its own ideas to meet the characteristics required by the General Board. But the bureau's vested interest in American technology and design affected its ability to adapt to new ideas or accept foreign technology.

Addressing the difficulty of obtaining quality submarines, Commander John H. Hoover of the CNO's Material Division (Submarine Desk) concluded in 1927 that the Navy Department simply had not invested enough time to educate the service and the public on the necessity of further submarine research and development. He doubted that naval authorities would neglect battleship ordnance in the same way because of the high level of consciousness in the fleet of the importance of this kind of hardware. Observing that naval officers and civilians would agree on the need to remain on the cutting edge of ordnance technology, the commander regretted that "we did not take advantage of the costly development work put into the submarine art by the Germans, and have today only submarines which were out of date before the Armistice, 8 years ago."[38] In a tone of exasperation he suggested that naval representatives go to Germany and purchase the plans for the latest, most seaworthy boat, or simply have one built. As Rear Admiral John Halligan, Chief of BUENG, put it in a comment before the General Board on 1 April, "we find in general that departures from German practice get us into trouble and that the trouble can generally be cured by strict adherence to German practice."[39]

The many viewpoints on submarine strategy and design first began to blend into a synthesis in the years between 1927 and 1930. An evaluation of America's responsibilities in the Pacific and Asia and a painstaking and detailed analysis of German strategy and design combined to produce the beginning of consensus.

In April 1927 one of the key figures in this first stage of consensus, Admiral Henry A. Wiley, then-Chairman of the General Board, sensed the possibility of a broad accord on design and strategy based on the characteristics of the larger German Ms-boats. If his intuition was correct, the General Board would be able to achieve a true concordance on submarine design and present a coherent, widely supported plan to the Secretary of the Navy for the first time since American entry into the Great War.

Aware of the dissatisfaction with submarine strategy and design among the operational forces, Wiley proceeded to compel BUC&R and BUENG to explore a 1500-ton design and promoted the 1175-ton U–135 as a basis for the discussion of specific characteristics. Rear Admiral George H. Rock, Assistant

Courtesy of the Naval Historical Foundation

Vice Admiral Henry A. Wiley.

NH 80542

39

Chief of BUC&R, objected to purchasing foreign plans or using foreign vessels as prototypes. He also resisted experimenting with the 1500-ton type and felt strongly that the General Board should define all of the military characteristics for new submarines before the bureau went to work on the design. However, the General Board held the authority to set required characteristics, so the technical bureaus had to give Wiley's suggestion serious consideration.

Shortly thereafter the Submarine Officers Conference followed Admiral Wiley's lead, adopting the U–135 as the standard for the future. Most of the officers present at the 2 June 1927 conference agreed on an all-purpose design of 900 to 1400 tons displacement. At 1175 tons, the World War I vintage U–135 fulfilled this requirement, giving the Navy a reliable prototype to copy. Lieutenant Commander Harold T. Smith of BUENG, a participant in the conference, even suggested building a duplicate of the U–135 for testing and evaluation before any new designs were considered for construction.[40]

Eight months later the accepted wisdom that submarines functioned most effectively either in coastal defense or when tied directly to the battle fleet came under fire. In February 1928 Commander Thomas Withers, Commander Submarine Division 4, openly challenged both roles by questioning the prudence of seeking a fleet submarine with greater speed. Preoccupation with this characteristic might adversely affect the habitability and submerged performance of future American submarines. More than any other vessel the submarine's restricted internal spaces ensured that any attempt to increase speed with larger engines and motors would have a profound impact upon other ship characteristics. Withers observed that the awkward maneuvering of the V–1 through 4 when submerged was an example. He argued that submarine divisions, then unable to perform reliably on the surface at 20 knots, could not serve in the supporting role assigned them by current strategic wisdom. Their slower pace would drastically increase the vulnerability of a fleet, while contributing little to the effectiveness of the capital ships in action. The commander argued that most submarine officers preferred independent operations to joint work with the fleet. This approach would allow the submarine to employ its stealth to best advantage in solo operations against enemy warships, a priority that would not eliminate intelligence gathering as a secondary mission.[41]

Moving to the Naval War College in 1930, the always quiet and amiable—but perceptive and precise—Withers further refined his ideas on submarine strategy. He urged naval planners and strategists to allow American submarines to adopt an exclusively offensive posture. If given the opportunity, Withers would allow the boats to operate independently in combined reconnaissance and attack missions. Rather than making exceptional speed the vital factor, Withers suggested that reliability, improved habitability, and long range would better serve the Navy. He recommended termination of the awkward attempts at perfecting a fleet boat, exemplified by the three 2000-ton behemoths that spearheaded the V class. This type should give way to smaller vessels capable of 15 knots on the surface, ninety days at sea, and a 12,000-mile range with satisfactory economy and dependability. Withers believed that a boat of approximately 900 tons could accomplish these ends with great practical benefits for the Navy.[42]

In a letter to Secretary of the Navy Charles Adams, the staff of the Naval War College supported the Withers viewpoint. Their research and study demonstrated that working directly with the fleet was the least important of the submarine's most essential missions.[43]

Once naval authorities started to seriously consider a role for the submarine that neither burdened it with coastal defense nor tied it to the battle fleet, the design debate took a completely new direction. Sensing their liberation from strategic confinement and the possibility of revising existing designs, the operational forces welcomed Withers's ideas. His new views proved very compatible with the position adopted by the SOC the previous year. For the first time in nearly ten years of postwar deliberations on submarine characteristics, the views of leading submarine strategists coincided with the opinions of the operational forces on the significant points of mission and displacement. In his statements before the General Board

National Archives, Bureau of Ships (RG 19)

Rear Admiral Thomas Withers attends the commissioning of *Tench* (SS–417) at Portsmouth Naval Shipyard, New Hampshire, 6 October 1944.

Rear Admiral Frank H. Schofield, Director of War Plans for the CNO, illustrated the strength of the new perspective by supporting the submarine characteristics suggested by Commander Withers and agreeing with the SOC that the U–135 design should serve as a basis for discussion.

Admiral Wiley's initiative in the spring of 1927 had provided an environment that encouraged new ideas and the exploration of their possibilities. After the SOC threw its support behind the U–135 design in June and confirmed his belief that a design accord was possible, the admiral continued to nurture the first signs of consensus. After leaving the General Board in November, Wiley became an enthusiastic advocate of Commander Withers's revisionist submarine strategy, only now from the more influential position of Commander in Chief, U.S. Fleet.[44]

With the hard-won experience gained from the S class and the U-boats, the Navy now seemed ready to recast the role of the submarine and to work with a displacement guaranteeing acceptable habitability, maneuverability, speed, and reliability—all within the limitations of current American diesel technology.[45] Thanks to Withers, Wiley, and the SOC, the last two V boats, the V–8 and V–9, displayed characteristics vastly different from the first vessels of their class, which represented the final attempt to achieve the large, classic fleet submarine.[46]

If the German experience played an influential role in shaping consensus on the characteristics of postwar American submarines, so did the considerable challenges of protecting and maintaining America's far-flung possessions, especially in the Pacific. Considerations of fleet operations and coastal protection often seemed to dominate the debate over which submarines to build. Nevertheless the necessity for long-range boats capable of reliable service emerged as a strong factor when appropriations began to shrink, and the Navy tried to do as much as possible with the few new vessels it could build.[47] It was the necessity for transpacific operations by its submarines that led the Navy to explore the German U-cruiser designs in the V–5 through 7.

For commanders with a prospect of service in the South Pacific or the Orient, speed and performance with the fleet took second place to mechanical reliability and range.[48] The S-class boats could not meet these needs. Initially built for high surface speed in a wartime effort to approximate the ideal fleet submarine, they proved an utter failure from the standpoint of operational reliability. This situation stemmed from major flaws in Electric Boat's Nelseco diesels.[49] Without a reliable diesel, a true transpacific submarine was out of the question. The pressure on the Bureau of Engineering to perfect the Bu-MAN diesel therefore increased, as did the search for better alternatives from the private sector.[50]

These vessels also failed to provide enough space and ventilation to keep the crew healthy and alert on long, hot Pacific voyages. Habitability therefore made the attributes of the U-cruiser appealing for American submariners.

These considerations meant that range, dependability, habitability, and solo operation would play a large part in defining the Navy's future submarines and would eventually help the technical bureaus and the SOC shape the possible consensus detected by Admiral Wiley. This new direction excited both those in the Navy eager for an effective submarine and those in private industry, which was in the throes of the Depression and desperate for new construction to end the long interwar dry spell.

In September 1930 the BUC&R proposed designs for the V–8 and V–9, *Cachalot* (SS–170) and *Cuttlefish* (SS–171), derived from perceived shortcomings in the U–135. After carefully examining the U-boat design, BUC&R concluded that the Germans must have built a vessel about 40 tons heavier than the weight specified in the plans. If the bureau remained completely faithful to the original German concept, ideal crew and storage spaces would shrink and the boat's small size would impede access to the propulsion plant for overhaul and repair. The original design displacement would also inhibit comfort in the tropics as well as operational stability, both on the surface and submerged.

Consequently the designers at BUC&R developed their own variations on the U–135 type. The London Naval Treaty of 1930 was an added incentive for pursuing an intermediate displacement. It stipulated a limit of 52,700 for the U.S. Navy's total operational submarine tonnage. If the 1175- to 1200-ton imitations of the U–135 could successfully incorporate the elements now considered most important, then BUC&R could build many more of the vessels and still remain within the limits of the treaty.[51]

Four schemes emerged from BUC&R deliberations over just how to adapt an intermediate design displacing from 1175 to 1500 tons for American service in the V–8 and V–9.[52] In Scheme A, the original concept of an enlarged U–135 changed little save for an increase in the diameter of the inner hull of the double-hull design to secure greater living and storage space in addition to greater submerged stability. Scheme B provided more control-room space, with increased accommodations for crew and refrigeration and a greater degree of accessibility to the engines. Both plans suggested using the Bu-MAN engines built at the New York Navy Yard to ensure reliability and long service with a minimum of repair and overhaul time.[53]

The introduction of new lightweight diesels by the Germans during the interwar period also affected the thinking at BUC&R and BUENG. Scheme C incorporated most of the features of the first two schemes, but this time these lighter engines took the place of the Bu-MAN machinery. However, BUENG still considered this engine risky and experimental when compared to the New York Navy Yard's well-tested product. Scheme D offered the 1560-ton V–7, still under construction at Portsmouth, as a control factor in the process of selection.

Through all of BUC&R's deliberations a new consensus carried the day, which combined the first stage forged by Admiral Wiley between 1927 and 1930 with the influence of the U-cruiser concept. BUC&R chose a slightly increased size to insure general utility; improved seakeeping qualities, reliability, and habitability; a 17-knot surface speed; and a minimum radius of 7500 miles. Although the consensus seemed complete at 1200 tons, the Submarine Officers Conference persisted in its advocacy of a slightly larger vessel that could more comprehensively incorporate features to enhance handling and habitability. Many officers also felt that the diverse missions assigned to the submarine required more than one type. Thus in the final stage of building a consensus, the technical bureaus, the SOC, and the General Board weighed the relative merits of a 1200-ton intermediate design, larger models ranging from 1450 to 1750 tons proposed by the SOC, and the continued proposals for coastal defense and mine-laying boats.[54]

The argument of the operational officers for a larger, alternative submarine or a variety of submarine types did not endanger the growing consensus as much as it revealed a dogged attachment to the traditional division of strategic responsibility between the coastal and fleet submarine. In reports to the General Board in February 1934, both Commander Sherwood Picking, Inspector of Machinery at Groton, and Lieutenant Commander Charles W. Styer, commander of *Cuttlefish* and a member of the Submarine Officers Conference, discussed fleet, minelayer, cruiser, and coastal submarines. Both officers saw vessels 300 tons heavier than the U–135 performing every task except coastal defense. The image of the submarine as a coastal defense vessel had clearly survived the 1930 Withers-Naval War College revision of the

NH 63417

Salmon (SS–182) on speed trials in 1938.

submarine's primary role. However, the prevailing opinion among operational commanders assigned nearly every major operational function to slightly larger boats, which were a synthesis of the 1100- to 1200-ton U–135 type with the larger U-cruiser.[55]

By 1934 a design of approximately 1500 tons had assumed the primary place within the submarine community as the best size and configuration to satisfy the desire for reliability, range, and habitability. BUENG and BUC&R could more easily accommodate the characteristics desired by the SOC and the General Board in this boat than in the 1100- to 1200-ton type suggested earlier. The success and popularity of the *Salmon* (SS–182)-*Sargo* (SS–188) design in the fleet testified to a final consensus achieved within the Navy by 1936.[56] The SOC, with no opposition from the technical bureaus, quickly rejected a suggestion by the General Board's persistent one-man submarine subcommittee, Chairman Rear Admiral Thomas Hart, that smaller and simpler boats could still play a major role in the submarine design evolution in America. In response the SOC forcefully declared:

> It was the unanimous opinion of the Submarine Officers' Conference that the requirements for submarines as approved by the Secretary of the Navy on 17 March 1936 will be better met by a 1450-ton submarine of the Sargo-Salmon type. . . . The Conference further feels that it is not prepared to scrap several years of progressive work and study of the Submarine Officers' Conference and respectfully adheres to its former opinion that the needs of the submarine service and the requirements of the Fleet are best met by a submarine of the Sargo-Salmon characteristics.[57]

In March 1936 the General Board's final recommendations to the Secretary of the Navy for the 1937 construction program gave 1450 tons as the "minimum compatible with a proper balance of the required military characteristics to meet the intended employment of the submarine."[58] At last the debate was over.

Observations

The primary strategic concepts that defined the submarine's role in the Second World War emerged from dissatisfaction with interwar American technology. The inability of current types to fulfill the mission assigned to the fleet submarine led imaginative officers like Withers to look for practical and more productive alternatives. By 1936 the bureaus and operational forces had reached a consensus on the vital issues regarding design that had sustained the interwar debate fueled by Stirling and Withers. In spite of a lasting devotion in some quarters to smaller craft, competition between the designs for the 800-ton coastal boats and the 2000-ton fleet boats resulted in their demise. Instead the 1450- to 1500-ton design emerged as the overwhelming preference of the SOC, the technical bureaus, and the General Board.[59]

After 1928 fewer naval planners tied the submarine's mission to the surface strategies conceived for the battle fleet. Instead the idea of independent patrols, offensive operations against enemy vessels, and intelligence-gathering pushed the old, direct fleet-support role further down the list of priorities and with it the concept of the fleet submarine as originally conceived.[60]

By the time the Seventy Percent Expansion Act of 1940 signalled the end of America's commitment to the weight restrictions imposed by the London Treaty of 1930, the Navy Department knew exactly what kind of submarine it wanted to build in quantity. The success and popularity of the *Salmon-Sargo* design set the stage for the mass production of the *Gato* (SS–212) and *Drum* (SS–228) types by the Electric Boat Company, Portsmouth Naval Shipyard, and Mare Island Naval Shipyard that commenced in 1940. The Navy would enter the world war in 1941 with a much better idea of the submarine's appearance and role than it had in 1919.[61]

3

A Firm Foundation?

I'd like to know from whom and where you expect to buy this boat.

—Commander Emory S. Land, 17 February 1919.

From the beginning building submarines in the United States resembled a tug of war between the Navy's technical bureaus and Electric Boat and Lake, two companies determined to retain both the initiative in submarine technology and the financial rewards it would bring. The private sector's reluctance to relinquish its advantage did not stem simply from a crass desire for monopoly and profit. Rather, the naval-industrial relationship suffered from a fundamental difference between the two contracting parties' perceptions of their mission.[1]

Thus the Navy and industry built the relationship that governed submarine construction from 1916 to 1940 on a foundation of misunderstanding. This conflict was exacerbated by mobilization for war, the constantly changing state of submarine technology, the virtual monopoly of the private sector market by one prime contractor, and the Navy Department's painfully slow definition of what it wanted in a submarine.

By 1940, however, this relationship improved considerably. Serious efforts to resolve the conflicts between the Navy and industry and the evolution of a consensus on submarine strategy and design contributed to a mature command technology for submarines. During the interwar period the Bureau of Construction and Repair had decided to utilize its meager financial resources to convert its Portsmouth Naval Shipyard into a state-of-the-art facility for submarine design and construction. This decision contributed significantly to the demise of Lake in 1924 and to the hardships borne by EB and made the bureaus more sensitive to the challenges facing private industry during a time of sharply reduced naval appropriations.

Government and Industry: Differing Viewpoints

The Secretary of the Navy and the technical bureaus viewed the construction of a submarine, or indeed any vessel, as the acquisition of a tool designed to support the Navy's activities in wartime. From this perspective the design, construction, and reliable operation of submarines became an evolving effort to place the best naval hardware at the disposal of the fleet. No single design, no matter how well conceived, completely fulfilled all the needs of the operational forces. If a submarine did not perform well, then the development of an improved design became an urgent matter. Even when designs did meet expectations, improvement continued.

Industry did not share this unrestrained long-term commitment to development, mission, and operational support. Electric Boat and Lake had to weigh the costs and responsibilities of this kind of commitment against their own goals and economic well-being. Thus they needed to define precisely their short- and long-term agreements with the Navy for submarine design and construction. EB and Lake believed that if the price and the contract agreement promised both profit and growth, the quality of their products would improve and the Navy would therefore benefit.

From industry's standpoint interaction with the Navy on any given vessel ended with the Navy's acceptance of the product, thus marking fulfillment of the contract. If the contract included terms that provided for correcting performance and design deficiencies or upgrading systems, then the contractor made those changes as well.

Unfortunately, submarine technology changed almost daily and the bureaus often discovered significant problems long after signing the initial contract. In such situations the technical bureaus argued that industry had a responsibility to render the submarine safe, dependable, and effective even after the contract had expired. Electric Boat and Lake, however, found complete satisfaction in fulfilling their contract to the letter and saw no reason to commit themselves further. If BUC&R or the Bureau of Steam Engineering wanted changes made or improvements developed and incorporated, a new agreement was in order and the Navy would have to pay for the additional services.

In this environment, defining a relationship to govern the construction of a vessel whose systems and design frequently changed proved extremely difficult.

Electric Boat Company

The Navy's first real effort as a submarine design organization came with the S-class plans in 1916. The Navy followed up by building the S–3 at Portsmouth to display its skill to the private sector. The potential competition bothered EB. Officials in BUC&R and BUENG feared the creation of a monopoly in the submarine construction market when Electric Boat received the T- and S-class contracts in 1916. To document their concern, these two bureaus wrote a joint memorandum to the Secretary of the Navy. They quoted EB correspondence to the effect that the Groton firm alone could produce a quality submarine; newcomers to the market would merely reduce the quality of the product. To Rear Admirals David Taylor and Robert S. Griffin in command at BUC&R and BUENG respectively, this attitude demonstrated "that it is the desire of the Electric Boat Company to maintain a monopoly in building submarines, and this is their major objection to the present contract and specifications and to the preparation of plans [for the S class] in the Department."[2]

Commitment to the fifty-boat S class and the heightened importance of the submarine after 1914 led the Navy Department to challenge EB's efforts to exercise a monopoly. In 1919 Lieutenant Commander Percy T. Wright, who was in charge of the Industrial Department at Portsmouth, supported the decision of the Board of Inspection and Survey to expect a higher quality submarine from Portsmouth; this way the Navy would gain a genuine alternative to the private sector. The S–3 would undergo all of the tests expected of a boat built in the private yards because, in Wright's words, "the principal reason, or at least one of the principal reasons, for the Government building and designing submarines was to force private concerns to give us what we wanted and to demonstrate to them that the Government could do the job successfully."[3]

To a friend at the Bureau of Navigation, Wright conveyed the frustration of the submarine community in the face of Electric Boat's strong position in the market. With the end of the war, the demand for submarines had declined, and he feared the bureaus would permit EB to swallow up the few available contracts.

Wright contended that in its effort to improve planning and construction, the Navy frequently underestimated its available assets. Portsmouth was a naval facility with an excellent design team operating in the Navy's interest. He believed that Portsmouth would respond far more quickly and sympathetically to any suggestions from the operating forces that might benefit the fleet. Wright lamented that some naval engineers and designers resigned at Portsmouth after the war because they assumed the bureaus would allow EB to dominate the field. He feared that, without additional

NH 46672

Steel racks and iron storage at Portsmouth Naval Shipyard, 1919.

NH 46675

New submarine ways under construction at Portsmouth, 1917.

support from the Navy, Portsmouth would lose a cadre of excellent technical people and the chance to offer Electric Boat genuine competition.[4]

Captain George W. Williams of the Submarine Section in the Office of the Chief of Naval Operations shared Wright's opinions and fears. In a memorandum to the CNO in February 1921, Williams argued in favor of awarding the first V-class fleet submarines to Portsmouth. He supported his case by citing EB's poor record for on-schedule construction and its general unsatisfactory performance in certain specific areas such as diesel propulsion.

He also argued that the poor performance of the S-class boats built by EB had the operational forces in revolt. "Ever since our submarine service has been in existence there has been dissatisfaction on the part of our operating personnel with the objectives, ethics, and results of the Electric Boat Company." He questioned the firm's objection to the presence of an operational submariner on a special board considering the company's claims for extra financial compensation because of the extraordinary circumstances created by the war.[5] Did the company fear the opinions of those who fought with the tools EB created?

This concern, voiced by Williams and shared by many in the operational forces, illustrated the fundamental clash of viewpoints between industry and the Navy. Captain Williams observed: "The objective of the Company has been to make money, to build submarines which would pass certain specified tests, not to build efficient fighting machines." Neither Williams nor many of the operational officers relished the idea of relying on T- and S-class EB submarines at sea when their lives hung in the balance.

Many within the Navy agreed with Wright and Williams that Portsmouth would more readily disseminate the technology and techniques of submarine construction while offering a viable alternative to Electric Boat.[6]

Lake Torpedo Boat Company

In June 1918 Simon Lake wrote to the Secretary of the Navy arguing for a fair share of the last nineteen submarines in the American construction program launched in 1916. He painstakingly outlined his company's capability and plans for the future. His Bridgeport construction facilities could build both 500- and 800-ton submarines. Completion of the S–3 and the R–21 through 27 by November 1918 would free seven 500-ton slips and one 800-ton slip for new construction. In response to the requirements of the larger S class, Lake had already laid plans for converting the 500-ton slips to accommodate the new 800 types, as well as allocating another 3,000 feet of waterfront for new submarine construction. The company had a staff of 1,800 skilled managers and workers ready to form the nucleus of an expanded facility that could satisfy the needs of the operating forces.

Given Lake's past history of poor management, this last resource did not impress the technical bureaus as much as the firm's long-term contract with the Busch-Sulzer Brothers Diesel Engine Company. Busch-Sulzer's remarkably dependable engines stood in contrast to the utterly unreliable

NH 46686

A 1917 interior view of a submarine model shed at Portsmouth Naval Shipyard.

NH 46541

L–8 (SS–48) under construction at Portsmouth, April 1916.

diesels of EB's Nelseco subsidiary. With its skilled personnel, expanded facilities, and Busch-Sulzer engines, Lake claimed that it could commit to ten 800-ton S boats immediately and possibly thirty to forty submarines per year in the near future.[7]

Lake had anticipated that the wartime submarine construction program would continue for many months. When the war ended in November, however, it quickly became apparent that the demand for submarines would decline and a battle would ensue for the few postwar contracts available.

In February 1920 the Navy Department ordered an evaluation of Lake's potential as an effective submarine contractor. The strength of EB's virtual monopoly and the possibility of using Portsmouth as the primary alternative to Electric Boat placed Lake in a vulnerable position. Was this contractor worth supporting, given the promise of Portsmouth and the advantage of having a government-controlled lead yard rather than another private-sector yard?

The board appointed by the Secretary of the Navy to look at the situation found Lake to be small and poorly equipped by industry standards. Because Lake specialized in submarines, which constituted 98.5 percent of its output, the board expected that the firm's expertise would offset increased costs due to antiquated or inadequate equipment. On taking a closer look, however, the board discovered that Lake recorded abnormally high construction costs for its nine S boats.[8] The company also took four to five months longer than the Bethlehem Shipbuilding Corporation at Quincy, the major subcontractor for

EB, to build its R-class vessels. The board also criticized Lake's plant layout and management, characterizing the plant floor supervisory force as "uninspired." The board concluded "that the Lake Company in building submarines on cost-plus-percentage contracts under the present management is continuously costing the Government large sums of money without adequate return." Members suggested ways to improve Lake's ability to compete; the suggestions amounted to a complete restructuring of the company's management. The board also felt that if Lake neglected to implement its recommendations in a reasonable time, the government should step in to assume control of the company.[9]

By April 1920 it became evident that the Navy was more interested in developing Portsmouth into a shipyard on par with EB than in supporting Lake. The latter had received only a handful of the S class contracts, and after the war no others seemed forthcoming. On behalf of his Bridgeport constituents, Senator Frank Brandegee (R–Connecticut) appealed to the Secretary of the Navy. He questioned the wisdom and necessity of allowing the highly specialized workers at Lake's Bridgeport facility to lose their jobs as a result of BUC&R's preference for awarding the few available postwar submarine contracts to EB and Portsmouth.[10]

Unfortunately for Lake, its performance did not give the Navy enough reason to reconsider its reliance on EB and Portsmouth. Lake's boats exhibited poor diving qualities, and the company had great difficulty keeping submarine construction on schedule. Captain Williams identified a major problem when he commented: "The Lake Company has been kept going by the Government and it has shown a disposition to do good work, but I understand that the company's business management has not been all that it should be and there have been long delays in the completion of work."[11]

In 1921, even as BUENG fought with EB over submarine diesels, Simon Lake wrote an open letter to Congress arguing for the survival of his company. He contended that his submarines had a high record of success in operational performance. He added that further investment in the experience and skill of his employees made sense, especially when Electric Boat displayed a lack of seasoning and competence in diesel engine design. Why should the Navy spend good money to re-engine boats purchased from EB? Lake would do the job right the first time, especially when it involved the diesel propulsion plant.

In May Captain Williams composed a memo for the Chief of Naval Operations in which he placed the Lake case in much broader perspective. He acknowledged that the performance of the company had improved in recent days, but maintained that

> the influences of the Lake Torpedo Boat Company and the Electric Boat Company have been the most potent in getting Congress to authorize submarines for the navy; but the motive behind their efforts, the desire to make money, has had its natural consequence. We got vessels which would pass

acceptance tests but were not efficient fighting machines.

Williams counseled the CNO to either seek authorization for the Navy to absorb Lake's facility or ask Congress to appropriate money for another six submarines, three of which Lake might receive if the bids were competitive. He wanted to preserve Lake in some form, if only as competition for EB, because "the prospect of a monopoly in submarine work by the Electric Boat Company is appalling."[12]

In spite of its best efforts the Secretary of the Navy could not extract additional funds from Congress. This predicament forced naval officials to choose among supporting Lake with one or two of the scarce V-class contracts, absorbing the company, or pushing it out of the market altogether by expanding the role of Portsmouth. BUC&R chose the last option, wishing to provide the Navy with a viable alternative to EB, and Portsmouth with the opportunity to develop vital skills and experience.

The diversity of EB's capabilities and its ship-construction experience permitted it to survive the long dry spell between 1921 and the contract for the V–9 in 1931. In the interim the company built everything from pleasure boats to machinery. The absence of the same diversity at Lake, combined with BUC&R's determination to help Portsmouth mature into a first-class submarine yard, assured the demise of the Lake Torpedo Boat Company. Simon Lake closed his small Bridgeport firm in 1924.

The Effect of Mobilization and War, 1916–1921

Neither the Navy nor the private sector accurately anticipated the impact of mobilization and war on their ability to work together. The Navy's responsibility seemed fairly well defined. The number of submarines had to increase, and the O, R, L, T, and S classes would receive priority. With the declaration of war in 1917 Congress freely financed such accelerated construction. The Navy Department believed the private sector had all it needed to accomplish the task with the proper amount of naval supervision.

Unfortunately this premise left too many unanswered questions. Were the raw materials available to satisfy the demands of the wartime economy? Did the necessary skilled labor exist to make the boats a reality? Did EB and Lake have sufficient capital to bear the burden of initial construction? How high did the government expect the cost of production to rise in wartime America?

Neither the Navy nor the private sector had given these problems much thought before the conflict actually began. Indeed not even in the Civil War had America attempted mobilization on this scale, and the effort needed took the entire nation by surprise. Many in both industry and government felt that the war would have a minimal effect on daily business. The director of the U.S. Council on National Defense, Grosvenor Clarkson, asserted after the war that each company and each part of the Armed Forces involved in war production went its own way and followed its own policy, resulting in costly confusion. Even after the July 1917 creation of the War Industries Board, designed to bring some order to resource allocation and price and wage controls, it took an executive order by President Wilson on 4 March 1918 to force the nation's industry and military to heed the call for central direction.[13]

The environment created by mobilization exacerbated the suspicion and mistrust that already characterized the naval-industrial relationship. Just as the private sector encountered the difficult labor and material problems generated by the war and the government introduced central direction of the war effort, the Navy and Electric Boat entered the intense and acrimonious argument over the flawed Nelseco diesels. The Navy Department, convinced before the war that the private sector would always pursue profit over national defense, now hardened its position on delays, schedule extensions, fixed prices, and bonus deadlines. These circumstances set the submarine industry, especially EB, on the defensive and seemed to confirm for many naval authorities all of their worst expectations regarding the Navy's prime submarine contractors.

The trauma of mobilization and the diesel debate set the mood for naval-industrial interaction from 1916 through 1921. EB and Lake quickly realized that mobilization and the intense competition for materials precipitated by the initial absence of central controls would have a detrimental effect on construction schedules and bonuses for early delivery. Unlike the navy yards, they competed as independent contractors on the open market for materials and labor. They could not hide under a protective government mantle in their effort to procure construction materials at reasonable prices. As a government facility, Portsmouth did not have to insure its product. Naval construction contracts required private contractors to provide their own insurance. Neither did the navy yards face the prospect of substantial fines for late delivery that constantly worried the private firms.[14]

The bureaus signed many submarine contracts with Lake and EB before American entry into the war. These agreements, finalized during the last months of peace, proved completely inadequate in the face of government intervention in the labor and raw materials markets, altered construction priorities, and emergency transport regulations that came into being once war was declared.

In one case EB's directors complained bitterly about prewar fixed-price contracts for parts that continued in force after the conflict began. Under a cost-plus-percentage contract EB had to pay what the market would bear. But often the technical bureaus and Navy Department did not appreciate the degree to which a war could inflate domestic prices. The company ran the risk that the Navy Compensation Board would refuse to approve a rate EB obtained on the open market when purchasing materials and skills for submarines like the S–18 through 41.[15]

As orders inundated the shipyards, Electric Boat and Lake increased their labor force dramatically. Because submarine construction requires highly skilled labor, EB and Lake immediately encountered major difficulties. New men on the work force did not have the same refined skills and experience as shipyard veterans. The yards complained to BUC&R that the dilution of expertise would dramatically affect work schedules and production. It might take months to educate new submarine workers properly, and in the process the contractors would probably fall behind schedule. The Navy's official construction priorities further complicated matters by drawing skilled labor from submarine projects for destroyer work.

The demands and momentum of war placed industry in a truly unenviable position. The Navy Department wanted more submarines, and it wanted them faster, but the burdens placed upon Lake and EB by mobilization militated against meeting these goals. In an atmosphere of increased demand and extraordinary economic conditions, industry had to expand available physical plant, pay overtime according to wartime wage regulations, increase administrative and supervisory staffs, and fight constantly for the delivery of required materials. EB and Lake often requested compensation for the losses caused by late delivery or lost bonuses because of these unusual wartime conditions. Nevertheless, the Navy Department routinely delayed settling these claims until the end of the war.[16]

The Navy's lack of understanding for the difficulties experienced by industry during mobilization brought some businesses close to ruin. The California Shipbuilding Company, for example, entered the submarine market as a major hull subcontractor for Lake before the United States entered the war. The high cost of labor and materials during the war and the absence of sufficient contract awards drove the Long Beach firm out of submarine construction.[17] The more experienced Electric Boat Company adjusted to the circumstances of the war by reallocating its most skilled labor according to company priorities. It also convinced BUC&R to minimize its frequent design modifications to the O-, T-, R-, and S-class vessels so that construction could proceed uninterrupted.[18]

With the trials created by the wartime economy and the fluid nature of submarine design during these years, EB argued that it could not work effectively under these adverse conditions unless naval authorities adopted a more liberal policy toward contract schedules and bonus deadlines. The private sector needed more time, capital, and incentive to compensate for the extraordinary financial drain caused by wages and prices regulated by the government outside the marketplace, designs subject to frequent alterations, inexperienced labor, and cash bonuses made available only after delivery.[19]

The Navy reacted to EB's viewpoint by displaying a resentment born of what it considered questionable business practices, poor attention to work, and improper supervision of production. Captain Henry Williams (CC), Superintending Constructor at Bethlehem Shipbuilding Corporation, reflected this attitude in a note to the Board on Submarine Claims in July 1920. In his eyes EB exaggerated the delays necessary to incorporate Navy modifications in the O and R classes during the war in order to obtain extensions that would allow it to capture early delivery bonuses. These rewards had become even more important to the company when the T and S-class boats experienced a variety of difficulties in construction and trials.[20] EB could offset some of the penalties for the poor performance of the newer submarine models by earning the bonuses on the O and R boats.[21] Williams also complained that EB even filled British orders for H-class submarines before American requirements and that all of the company's projects suffered from poor supervision and inadequate attention to detail.

In the few instances when the Navy did catch EB concentrating its resources on the bonus submarines, official indignation stemmed less from the practice itself than from the fundamental difference in naval and industrial perspectives.[22] The company's pursuit of the bonuses attached to the O and R boats only seemed to confirm the Navy's misgivings regarding the private sector's motives. The technically flawed Nelseco engines and EB's defensive attitude toward Navy criticism seemed to provide further evidence. The war demanded that the Navy fulfill its mission, and the private sector

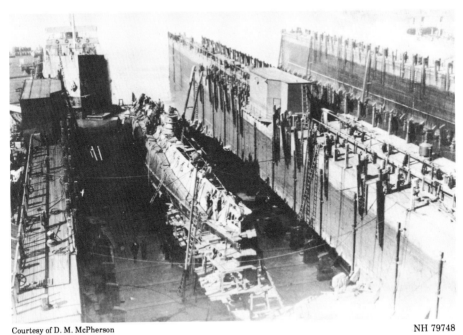

Courtesy of D. M. McPherson   NH 79748

R–15 (SS–92) under construction at Union Iron Works in San Francisco, 1918.

seemed preoccupied with finding excuses for poor quality diesels and deficient workmanship. It made no difference that neither the Navy nor EB fully understood the torsional vibration problem that actually plagued the Nelseco diesels. The circumstances of mobilization and the propulsion problem seemed to confirm each group's worst fears about the other.

Personalities and institutional pressures certainly accounted for the often uncompromising attitudes taken by the Navy and EB. These factors included the temperaments of individuals in opposing roles—the Navy's Supervisor of Shipbuilding and his counterpart in private industry, the company project manager. Potential confrontations often turned into constructive compromises if a Supervisor of Shipbuilding was sensitive to the pressures being experienced by the company, or if a company executive could appreciate the Navy's position.

Postwar Compensation Claims

All the confrontations and accommodations between the public and private sector formed part of the evolution of a mature command technology for submarines. Industry's postwar claims for compensation provide an interesting opportunity to view naval-industrial interaction. In 1919 the Electric Boat Company filed claim with the Navy for compensation, citing extraordinary conditions and naval wartime priorities for its excessive expenditures on the T, O, R, and S classes. The company had endured the reduction in profit during the conflict pending settlement of claims at the end of the war as promised by the technical bureaus and the Secretary of the Navy.

The case involved more than $7 million, a substantial amount by any standard, so the Navy appointed a board to investigate the legitimacy of the claim. The officers assigned to the investigation, led by Captain William J. Baxter (CC), found the demands so interrelated that they examined them together in the context of the company's internal corporate structure, history, and international business relationships.[23]

The approach to EB's claims is perhaps the most interesting factor in this process of settling the Navy's wartime financial obligations. The Baxter board placed Electric Boat under a microscope. The company's relationship with the Submarine Boat Corporation, the parent company established by EB directors to secure the firm from hostile takeovers, was explored. The Navy also looked carefully at EB's responsibility for its Nelseco, Electric Launch Company (Elco), and Electro-Dynamic Company affiliates as well as its close business association with the General Ordnance Company, National Torpedo Company, and the Vanadium Metals Company.[24]

Electric Boat's claims specified six instances in which excessive expenditures were caused by circumstances beyond its control. The six included changes authorized by the bureaus during construction, increased wages mandated by the Macy board, the premature launching of the R–1 through 20 ordered by the Navy, extra police for shipyard security, and an allowance for retroactive wages.[25] The company received compensation for its increased security needs and for the time and expense taken to implement design changes. But the Baxter board took a hard line with regard to increased labor costs. The board also looked carefully at claims for lost bonuses or premiums because members suspected that this money would only add to corporate profits. In the end the board drastically reduced the amounts EB requested in each of the claims until the total amount fell from over $7 million to $3,392,023.

Electric Boat fared better after a review of the Baxter board's findings by a group of officers that included the senior member of the Compensation Board and the chiefs of BUENG and BUC&R. It increased the award after considering the effect of the conversion of some contracts from fixed price to cost-plus-percentage in 1917 and the influence of the war on the materials and labor market.[26]

A final review board chaired by Rear Admiral Taylor further adjusted the award amount, which by this time had reached $3,419,552, exceeding the Baxter board sum by nearly $30,000. The Navy granted more than the company had asked for on the wage and security police claims, but offered less than half of EB's early delivery premium request.[27]

This final award struck a balance between naval needs and the welfare of a vital contractor. The Navy compensated Electric Boat for wages and premiums to keep the company in the market and to allow a modest profit, recognizing the effect of war on the American economy. But by conducting such a thorough investigation and laying bare EB's corporate structure and relationships, the Navy now knew more than ever before about its difficult partner in the submarine construction business.

Construction Resumes

Between 1925 and the award of the *Cuttlefish* contract to EB in 1931, the private sector received no contracts for new construction, and the Portsmouth

National Archives 80–G–K–3350

Cuttlefish (SS–71), the V-class submarine built by Electric Boat, marked the end of a construction dry spell for private industry in 1931.

Naval Shipyard received only four. This compounded the difficulty of improving the facilities at Portsmouth and educating and refining the skills of the yard's work force. From 1917 through 1920 Lieutenant Commander Herbert S. Howard (CC), who would serve at the Bureau of Ships and direct the David Taylor Model Basin during the Second World War, assembled a fine design team at Portsmouth. But they received few opportunities for indispensable practical experience in new construction. The only positive by-product of these trying economic conditions was the Navy's deeper appreciation of the considerable economic challenges perpetually confronting the private submarine yards.

Early in his first term President Franklin Roosevelt acted in conjunction with Congress to increase naval spending. While strengthening the Navy the nation's leaders also hoped to encourage economic growth and promote employment. Thus, even before the Vinson-Trammel Act of 27 March 1934 granted congressional authorization for naval construction up to the London Treaty limits of 1930, the Roosevelt administration accelerated ship construction with emergency funds made available under the New Deal's National Industrial Recovery Act (NIRA).[28]

The London Treaty of 1930 imposed a limit of 52,700 tons on the submarine force, and the Navy projected that 24,810 tons currently in service would be hopelessly antiquated by the end of 1936. Thus in a first step toward reaching the London Treaty limits, the Navy began adding submarines to the fleet by providing its own funds for 2260 tons, or two boats, and looking to the NIRA to supply four more vessels at 5200 tons. Because congressional legislation stipulated a division of labor between the naval shipyards and EB, the Navy followed the *Porpoise* class of 1933 by assigning the newly authorized *Salmon* class to EB and the naval shipyards at Portsmouth and Mare Island.[29]

The struggle to revitalize and strengthen the submarine force seemed so similar to the mobilization of 1917 that the Navy applied many wartime techniques to the new construction program of the 1930s. It admonished the Board of Inspection and Survey to exercise great care in ensuring that ship specifications were met. The Navy also inflicted higher financial penalties on the private sector for defective workmanship. In one case the punishment for failing to achieve the proper metacentric height on submarines amounted to $2,000 for every one-inch variation between 12 and the required 14.4 inches.[30] Using substandard materials, disregarding the necessity to obtain authorization for extraordinary work, or simply ignoring the instructions of the subcontractor or naval representative on site brought further pecuniary penalties. As a matter of policy the technical bureaus regularly rejected any such practices. The Navy refused to repeat the awkward circumstances of 1914 through 1917 when industry enjoyed a free hand in design, construction, and the procurement of labor and materials.[31]

In some cases New Deal legislation like the NIRA placed extraordinary burdens on the private sector.[32] Designed in part to help the depressed American shipbuilding industry, these emergency measures often inflated construction costs to the dismay of many company officials. In a letter to the Inspector of Machinery and the Superintending Constructor at Groton, EB's vice president, L. Y. Spear, wrote that the company would file for compensation as a result of the higher wages EB had to pay because of new shipyard labor regulations. The firm's records revealed a cost overrun of $106,617 on *Cuttlefish* alone because of direct and indirect labor costs and delays directly attributable to government regulations.[33] Electric Boat continued, with little success, to fight the Navy for compensation on the *Cuttlefish* project through 1936. Then the company threatened to seek a legislative solution in Congress. Already uncomfortable with EB's control over numerous submarine patents and private-sector construction, neither the Navy nor Congress felt inclined to grant the settlement the company sought.[34]

In spite of the mutual suspicions aroused by such confrontations, by the late 1930s the Navy had developed greater sensitivity to the financial risks taken by the private yards. The burden on submarine companies increased when Congress passed the Vinson-Trammel Act of 1934, limiting the profit taken on any ship construction project to 10 percent of the contract award.[35] In his testimony before the House Committee on Naval Affairs, the Navy's

L. Y. Spear, Vice President of Electric Boat Company, 1902–1942.

NH 46910

Judge Advocate General, Rear Admiral Gilbert J. Rowcliff, acknowledged the high insurance rates, rising material and personnel costs, strikes and labor unrest, and the strict penalties for late or unsatisfactory work borne by industry.

Naturally, Electric Boat Company resisted any additional burdens the government asked it to bear. But unlike the situation in 1916, the company now confronted a Navy willing and able to have its own way by playing the role of senior partner. In 1938 L. Y. Spear wrote to his old acquaintance, Rear Admiral Thomas Hart, Chairman of the General Board, questioning the necessity of BUENG's instruction to submit each diesel engine proposed for use in submarines to a series of type standardization tests. In doing so, he revealed an intense desire to return to the time when his company had a free hand in submarine matters. Spear reasoned that if "we could be given a free hand in the design of the whole boat including the engines as we were in the old days, the necessity for the type test would disappear and the responsibility for the results would rest squarely on us where I think it should belong."[36]

This situation was exactly what the Navy wanted to avoid. When BUENG distributed a circular to bidders in March 1939 outlining the particulars of the propulsion machinery for new submarines, Spear sent another letter to Hart. The company vice president bemoaned the Navy's efforts to exert control over the design and production process. Spear felt that the Navy had challenged EB's understanding of the relative responsibilities of the Navy and industry in design and construction. He commented to Hart that

> the [Bureau of] Engineering circular as drafted would be very far from satisfactory to us. While it has been the understanding from the beginning that we would supply all of the propulsive equipment, the circular provides for the storage battery to be supplied by the Government. The circular literally interpreted would even prevent the use of the engine developed by us. On top of that it goes into innumerable details which have no place in the circular and which cannot be properly decided so far as our design is concerned at this time. These details can and should be taken care of in the special specifications; in other words the document drafted by [Bureau of] Engineering is practically a special specification instead of a circular.[37]

Hart responded diplomatically, assuring Spear that BUENG expected to work with EB on the design specifications and did not wish to inhibit discussion of the matter. Although Hart assured Spear that EB would not lose its "free hand," the admiral clearly implied that the Navy now preferred to take the lead in a team effort. The Navy Department and the technical bureaus had no wish to experience, once again, the solo performance given by the private sector before the war. Electric Boat would still play a vital role in the submarine construction program, but would now do so within the context of both the Navy's expertise in submarine technology and its substantial design and construction capability at Portsmouth. Hence from 1931 to 1940 teamwork with the Navy was EB's only option.[38]

Construction Accelerates

Beginning in 1937 Assistant Secretary of the Navy Charles Edison received authority from Secretary Claude Swanson to administer an accelerated construction program funded by New Deal recovery legislation and congressional budget appropriations. Earlier in the year Edison had advanced a general scheme designed to reduce the anticipated complexity of a new construction program while appealing to naval vendors, old and new. He suggested that, to raise quality, Portsmouth and Mare Island should compete with the private sector for contracts on the basis of construction cost and time. Edison also said the Navy should decentralize design and procurement and adopt longer production runs. Initiating major design changes every other year rather than annually would permit the Navy and the private sector to produce more submarines with the tools, machinery, and experienced workers already in place.

Edison had also recommended that the Navy persuade Congress to authorize partial exemptions to both the Walsh-Healy Act that governed the man hours spent per week on government contracts, and the Vinson-Trammel Act that authorized an increase in shipbuilding. The Navy would need some exceptions to these measures if it expected industry to find the submarine

Charles Edison, Assistant Secretary of the Navy, 1933–1939; Secretary of the Navy, January-June 1940.

NH 56986

construction business attractive and profitable. He also pursued the possibility of extending the work week up to twelve hours beyond the federally imposed limit of thirty-six hours on government shipbuilding contracts.

Finally, Edison believed the General Board of the Navy would have to define clearly the approved characteristics of any vessel by 1 January of each year. This precise determination of the Navy's desires, coupled with keeping design changes to an absolute minimum during construction, would give every contractor a far better grasp of what the Navy expected.[39]

Given complete authority by Secretary Swanson in 1938 to direct the increased shipbuilding program, Edison now put his ideas into practice. He issued orders to limit the number of design changes authorized by the technical bureaus during construction. Historically, these mid-stream modifications precipitated more slowdowns and delays in the construction process than did any other cause save diesel engine performance. Edison ruled that the yards could not implement any change requiring more than $10,000 or two weeks' work time without direct approval of the Secretary of the Navy.[40]

Edison then approached Rear Admiral Joseph R. DeFrees, former Commander Submarine Force, U.S. Fleet, on the best ways to expedite construction. DeFrees suggested improvements in three areas. After the experience of the 1920s, an uninterrupted construction program was absolutely necessary to develop the skills, facilities, tools, and workmanship necessary to sustain a submarine fleet. Secondly, he called for standard types so the submarine community could fulfill a strategy on the Withers model. The frequent design changes and lesser modifications, which produced numerous delays and deprived the operational forces of vital experience with dependable vessels, put the nation at risk. DeFrees complained that these delays were exacerbated by a lack of skilled labor and adequate facilities. In spite of the unemployment problem of the Depression years, shipbuilding trades and occupations had critical labor shortages. Lastly, shipbuilding projects needed more hours, fewer strikes, and more efficient utilization of skilled workers like draftsmen and engineers who could not operate in shifts.[41]

Heeding DeFrees's advice, Edison took steps to insure that the American shipbuilding industry and the Navy could provide the submarine fleet required in a world troubled by Nazi Germany and Imperial Japan. Between the Vinson-Trammel Act of 1934 and the second Vinson Act of 1938, Congress raised the authorized strength of the submarine force to fifty-six submarines, for a total of 81,956 tons. These measures would soon turn into appropriations for increased naval construction, so the assistant secretary took steps to augment industrial capability. He initiated apprenticeship and training programs to improve workers' skills and allocated resources for tools and replacement parts. Under his direction the Navy increased the number of engineers and draftsmen in its service by borrowing people from other agencies and training them for Navy work in cooperation with the Civil Service Commission. Continuing to tap both public and private expertise, Edison also decentralized the design of lead vessels in each class. Once a design proved successful, he centralized the design and drafting work for the subsequent ships of any class to avoid costly duplication.[42]

Mindful of DeFrees's anxiety over the limited facilities for submarine construction in the United States, Edison encouraged the further development of shipyard facilities suitable for submarine work. Within the Navy he laid plans to expand the services at Mare Island Naval Shipyard to support the construction efforts at Portsmouth. In the private sector he composed an agreement with EB in 1940 to enlarge dramatically the company's facilities in Groton, Connecticut, and Bayonne, New Jersey.

This arrangement provided EB with government appropriations to pay for a major expansion. The company in turn had to agree "that throughout the useful life of this facility, the Government will be given priority in the use thereof, and the facility will be preserved for National Defense purposes." A letter from Lewis Compton, Acting Secretary of the Navy, to EB on 23 September 1940 authorized $2.75 million for Electric Boat to expand its plant facilities in order to receive massive new submarine orders from the Navy.

Rear Admiral Joseph R. DeFrees.

NH 50537

EB had made it quite clear that if the Navy contemplated increasing its submarine fleet, the private sector would have a hard time rising to the challenge. The company refused to commit its own capital, fearful the market would evaporate once again as it did after the Great War. Because Portsmouth and Mare Island could not carry the burden alone, investment in EB seemed to be the Navy Department's best solution.[43]

In 1940 the Navy also managed to attract another private contractor to the submarine business as a support facility for EB. The Manitowoc Shipbuilding Company of Manitowoc, Wisconsin, entered into an agreement with the Navy in September 1940 to build EB submarine designs under license. The Navy had decided to pursue a long production run with the *Gato*-class submarines, and Manitowoc would provide the Navy with duplicates of the vessels produced by EB at Groton. Manitowoc would use *Growler* (SS–215) as a prototype and, with EB patents, supervision, training, and special systems installation, would build the SS–265 through 274 series.[44] The company prepared its Great Lakes plant to build these boats, and contracted with Inland Waterways Corporation to bring each completed vessel down the Mississippi on a barge from Lockport, Illinois.

The advantage of this arrangement was its speed, simplicity, and cost-effectiveness. Edison believed this arrangement would yield a large number of submarines while saving design and construction time, and the expense that new tools, equipment, spare parts, planning, and testing normally consume.[45]

The Manitowoc arrangement proved successful in spite of some difficulty with EB. Electric Boat cooperated with the Navy as the plan unfolded, but the company exhibited a degree of reluctance to extend to the new contractor all of the supervisory and technical assistance that the agreement required.[46] Although Electric Boat's directors negotiated for Manitowoc, the Groton facility would not place orders or guarantee that its private subcontractors would offer Manitowoc the same prices that EB paid on long-term projects.

The firm complied only reluctantly with BUSHIPS in the Manitowoc case because it took exception to the idea of aiding a possible competitor. In spite of this obstacle, on the strength of its investment in EB facilities and with the promise of new contract awards, the Navy molded the Groton company into a conduit for plans, procurement assistance, and technical expertise that streamlined the production of the seventy-three-boat *Gato* class.[47]

Observations

As America entered the First World War, the disadvantages of depending completely on a pair of private prime contractors soon became apparent. The Navy had to rely on Electric Boat and Lake for the technological expertise to build and maintain submarines, but each party's understanding of the obligations imposed by the construction contracts differed significantly. The

National Archives 19–N–31122

Keel laying of *Growler* (SS–215) at the Electric Boat Company, Groton, Connecticut, February 1941.

19–N–31129

Growler, built at EB, became the prototype design for all the Manitowoc-built submarines of the Second World War beginning with *Peto* (SS–265).

Navy sought to engage private industry in an open-ended, long-term effort to develop the most reliable submarine. The private sector wanted to help the nation build submarines but always within parameters strictly defined by a contract for each vessel. Working toward the same goal, but from different viewpoints, proved a confusing and turbulent experience for both sides.

After these differences became clearer under the pressures of mobilization and war, the Navy resolved not to depend so completely on private industry in the future and emerged from the construction dry spell of the interwar period with a greater degree of maturity. In the depressed submarine market after the First World War, the technical bureaus fulfilled their ambitious plans for Portsmouth and, in the process, caused the demise of Lake. These experiences taught the Navy the realities of the submarine construction business and spawned greater sensitivity to the pressures felt by the private sector. By the early 1930s the policies of Assistant Secretary Edison demonstrated both this new sensitivity and a determination to take the initiative and play the role of dominant senior partner in dealings with the private submarine industry. When the political and economic atmosphere of the 1930s allowed the construction of large numbers of new submarines to resume, the Navy created support yards for Portsmouth and EB at Mare Island and Manitowoc. These facilities guaranteed increased output and provided safeguards against the threat of monopoly by the private sector.

4

On-the-Job Training

Inasmuch as the S–10 to S–13 and the S–48 to S–51 are the latest submarines of the "S" type placed in service, it would appear to indicate that the problem of submarine construction is not as yet solved, as the defects in design and workmanship of these two late classes of submarines would appear to be more serious than those existing in older vessels.

—Board of Inspection and Survey, 15 April 1925

As America entered the Great War, the submarine represented the cutting edge of naval technology. Building the Navy's submarine fleet presented obstacles to the engineer and architect as strange and complex as the principles of battleship construction seemed familiar. Actually building submarines in large numbers helped the Navy quickly identify the major problems of design, engineering, and construction. The dilemma of efficiently enclosing the capability to live, breathe, observe, and attack in a severely restricted space turned the construction of each succeeding class of submarines into an independent research and development project. In addressing these difficulties, naval authorities used the modest appropriations available after the war to improve the Navy's design and construction capability at the Portsmouth Naval Shipyard and to advance private-sector submarine research and development. This policy not only provided the bureaus and the private sector with valuable opportunities for practical technical education, it also placed the Navy in the role of coordinator and catalyst for the first time.

Unfortunately, the Navy and its private contractors received this education during a period of dramatic fluctuation in the market for submarines. The extraordinary demand that came with mobilization for war presented many small, high technology firms with the opportunity and the need to expand production facilities. After barely two years of war these same companies, as well as many naval activities, were expected to survive a demobilization process that suggested a dismal future for submarine construction.

The quandary facing the Sperry Gyroscope Company in 1918 illustrates well the difficulties faced by the Navy and industry. Sperry manufactured gyrocompasses, fire control systems, stabilizers, and automatic navigation systems for surface ships and submarines. In his report on the company's postwar transition strategy, Vice President and General Manager P. R. Bassett noted that an "atmosphere of uncertainty and a tendency to 'mark time'" prevailed among the nation's top leaders in Washington, D.C. In this environment his company had to plan for survival.[1]

Sperry's wartime commitments had left it with substantial cash-flow problems and outstanding bank loans. These circumstances, compounded with impending cutbacks on naval orders and the possible cancellation of some current contracts, led Bassett to recommend that Sperry develop a carefully selected line of products that would insure an annual business volume of $3–4 million. This "transition business" would act as a source of badly needed revenue and a survival tool in the face of national defense budget reductions. Bassett urged immediate action on his suggestion, arguing that "*any* business with *any* profit will do." The government might provide part of the transition business, but, at best, the future was uncertain.[2]

The market for shipbuilding skills and related technology provided most private contractors with their only means of surviving the virtual absence of government business after the Great War. The need to endure in order to preserve profit and growth, as well as the capability for designing and building submarines in the United States, helped motivate industry and the naval submarine community during the interwar years.

Although the Navy and the private sector confronted similar circumstances after the war, each reacted in different ways. For submarine contractors like Sperry, Electric Boat, and Kollmorgen Optical Corporation (the Navy's periscope specialist), demobilization brought uncertainty and thus prompted retrenchment. The directors of these and other companies naturally called for a strategy to survive what promised to be a dramatic decline in naval ship construction.

Even with the expectation that appropriations for submarines would decrease, the Navy could not follow the retrenchment of the private sector. If the performance of Navy submarines was to equal that of the German U-boats in the war, the Navy would have to take over the initiative in design and development from private industry. Thus during the interwar period the technical bureaus as well as the operational submariners promoted and sponsored, as far as meager resources would allow, research on the development of diesel engines, armament and communications technology, periscopes, and habitability.[3]

Armament

During the Great War, American torpedo manufacturing underwent dramatic changes. The wartime G, K, E, M, H, L, N, and O classes, armed with four forward torpedo tubes, employed the standard 18-inch Mark 7 torpedo manufactured by Bliss-Leavitt Company of Brooklyn, New York, and the U.S. Naval Torpedo Station in Newport, Rhode Island.[4] The Mark 7 had a range of at least 3500 yards at 35 knots. With the advent of the Navy's R- and S-class designs, the General Board initiated a debate on the relative merits of continuing the Mark 7 or switching to a 21-inch variety called the

Mark 10. The latter carried a more powerful explosive charge and offered the added advantage of allowing both submarines and the surface fleet to use the same torpedoes.[5]

Beginning with the R class and continuing through the long production run of the S boats, the 21-inch Mark 10 became the standard submarine weapon of the 1920s and 1930s. It prevailed over the old 18-inch Mark 7 in spite of the powerful argument that the slimmer weapon would allow an increase in the bow tubes from four to six. Greater killing power proved the determining factor. In addition, standardizing the torpedoes used in the fleet made fiscal sense. The change to a greater diameter did not drastically affect the S-class boats under construction at Portsmouth, but it did require EB to make substantial structural changes to its submarines of the same class.[6]

With the introduction of the 21-inch system, the operational forces discovered that the shutters over the torpedo tube's outer doors presented the Navy with an unanticipated hydrodynamic problem.[7] When the new torpedoes left the tubes, the shutters would often damage the weapon's control surfaces. A 5/8-inch clearance usually allowed undisturbed passage. In this case, however, as the projectile proceeded out of the tube, the water rushing out with it caused the shutters to move inward a fraction of an inch. BUC&R suggested some design modifications, but the problem persisted. A twenty-day voyage in December 1924 from Guam to Pearl Harbor by the nine boats of the Submarine Division of the U.S. Asiatic Fleet disclosed eight defective shutters out of a possible thirty-six. None of these submarines could safely fire a torpedo without the possibility of a shutter casualty.[8] It took Portsmouth and EB until 1929 to devise the system for pinning back the shutters, which eliminated the problem.

Submarine deck ordnance proved less a technical problem than a function of the Navy's interwar debate over the vessel's mission. Would American submarines engage in a war against merchant traffic as German submarines did during the Great War? Should the submarine force operate in conjunction with the battle fleet? Was the submarine essentially a weapon of stealth and opportunity, too vulnerable to risk in surface encounters with armed merchant vessels and warships? Until 1940 these familiar questions sustained the discussion about the size and purpose of the deck gun.

When the idea of using deck-mounted torpedo tubes quickly died because of reloading and operational difficulties, the deck gun took center stage. During the war the O and R classes used, respectively, 3-inch, 23-caliber and 3-inch, 50-caliber models mounted forward of the conning tower. Although this location eventually gave way to a position aft of the tower, the caliber and size of the gun remained standard on all but the S boats until the Navy equipped the *Balao* class with 4-inch models after 1942.

Equipping the S class with 4-inch, 50-caliber guns reflected the debate over the mission of the American submarine as an instrument of offensive or

NH 42835

S-class submarines were equipped with 4-inch, 50-caliber guns like this one.

defensive engagement. Its designers definitely envisioned surface operations with the fleet and possible engagements with escort vessels. Indeed, the original 2000-ton, V-class fleet submarine designs called for even larger 5-inch, 51-caliber guns. This configuration would have transformed the first three boats of the V-class into submarine-destroyers, natural complements to the surface fleet. In their final form these vessels carried the old 3-inch gun because the weight of the larger type would have compromised their stability.

The Navy did not resolve the deck gun issue until the mid–1930s. The consensus reached between 1927 and 1936 on the size and role of the submarine set aside the heavier boat designs, the fleet support role, and with it the heavier guns. *Pike* (SS–173), *Shark* (SS–174), and *Perch* (SS–176) all carried 3-inch guns, as did the entire *Gato* class (SS–212 through 284) with which America entered the Second World War.[9]

Communication and Detection

During and after the Great War the Naval Research Laboratory (NRL) and a host of private contractors refined the radio and sound detection gear necessary to enhance the offensive power of the Navy's submarines. By 1923 submarine radios were deemed reliable for surface transmissions up to 300 miles. In one test of surface capability, the R–22 communicated with a vessel near Block Island from a location off Cape Hatteras without any difficulty.

Work at the NRL and General Electric Company in 1927 and 1928 produced effective high-frequency radio transmitters for submarines. The crystal-controlled, high-frequency XE transmitter allowed the V–1 and V–2 to communicate on the surface over distances of 200 to 500 miles depending on their positions and atmospheric conditions. Between 1930 and 1932 the Navy also equipped twenty S boats with the TAR transmitter, which better utilized the low power available on board submarines for radio communications. The TAR operated at both low and high frequency.[10]

Submerged communications presented a greater problem. In January 1920 an S-class boat received German transmissions from Europe while submerged at a depth of 14 feet off New London, Connecticut. By 1930 some of the V- and S-class submarines could receive transatlantic communications 64 feet below the surface. Although transmissions originating from submerged vessels initially proved more difficult, the broadcast range of the XE in 1928 and its successor XK in 1929 was about 80 miles. The Navy experimented with periscope and loop antennas to increase this range, abandoning the old French-coil type that was secured to the submarine bridge wings during the First World War.[11]

In the area of underwater sound detection, the Navy focused on antisubmarine warfare (ASW) during and after the war, relegating listening and detection devices for the submarine to second priority. Dr. Harvey C. Hayes and his underwater acoustics team at the Naval Experimental Station (NES) in New London formed the only group within the Navy doing research on underwater acoustics when America entered the war. Secretary of the Navy Josephus Daniels quickly drafted academic research in support of the Navy's wartime effort, and both NES and the navy yard at Key West provided testing grounds for the technology developed by universities and the Navy.

In the industrial sector, the Submarine Signal Corporation, General Electric Company, and Western Electric Company responded to war by pooling their research assets at the latter's Nahant facility in Essex County, Massachusetts. They excluded academic scientists to avoid patent complications and focused on hydrophone-based listening devices for surface vessels involved in ASW. As the war progressed, however, the Naval Experimental Station became the underwater acoustics coordinating facility not only for its own research, but also for that of private industry and the academic community, such as the Columbia University group led by prominent physicists R. A. Millikan and G. E. Hale.[12]

After the war financial resources dried up and the Hayes group once again became the only full-time research team devoted to underwater acoustics. All of the Nahant apparatus went to the Naval Experimental Station shortly before the entire Navy effort moved to the Engineering Experiment Station (EES) in Annapolis. In 1923 the Navy's acoustics team moved to the District of Columbia to set up shop in the newly created Naval Research Laboratory at Anacostia.

With the acceleration of submarine production in the 1930s, the NRL had more opportunities for operational tests with advanced hydrophones and different variations on active or pinging QC sonar. This system first appeared in surface ships in 1934. More practical experience with the Navy's newest 1450-ton submarines allowed the development of the JK/QC technique for the determination of target, range, and bearing. The passive, or listening JK sonar, which had replaced the SC hydrophones of the First World War, found and classified targets. The active QC sonar worked in the single ping mode to obtain their range and bearing. The system was reliable within 800 yards, which increased to 5000 by 1939.[13]

Periscopes

Officers also needed quality optical instruments, or they ran the risk of squandering the advantage of surprise. The periscope, just like the components of sound-communication and detection systems designed to complement submarine weaponry, involved the Navy with technology that private industry had pioneered.

From the beginning, the private sector designed and built all Navy periscopes. On earlier classes of submarines, these instruments remained at a fixed position and power. Bausch and Lomb Optical Company, Keuffel and Esser Company, and General Ordnance, a company closely associated with Electric Boat, had manufactured the periscopes that went to war in the E-, K-, L-, and O-class boats.

With the growing significance of the submarine, the need for working periscopes, capable of movement and adjustment, naturally increased. In 1916 Frederick Kollmorgen, an optical designer with Keuffel and Esser, decided to capitalize on this demand by forming his own company in conjunction with the Eastern Optical Company of New York City. Kollmorgen had emigrated from his native Germany to Vienna, where he refined his skills on the staff of optics pioneer Karl Reichert. He then came to America via England, working for a time in London with Ross, Ltd. Kollmorgen's working periscopes employed imported French optical glass and the latest scientific knowledge to produce the best periscope optical sets in the United States.

In its first year of operation the Kollmorgen Company became a regular Navy subcontractor for working periscopes on the strength of its founder's American patents secured in 1911. Frederick Kollmorgen's first Navy contract was a handwritten letter from BUC&R for the two periscopes destined for the K–1 at a price of $1,385 and $1,685.

The Navy introduced the first working periscope with the K-class submarines, all built by EB subcontractors between 1912 and 1914. The Kollmorgen type ordered for the K–1 (SS–32) in 1916 was capable of the now

NH 52200

K–8 (SS–39) was equipped with Type C, vertical-moving Kollmorgen periscopes.

familiar vertical movement and a 1.2 power magnification setting.[14]

The magnitude of wartime demand and scarcity of qualified contractors presented a perpetual problem. In February 1918 Bausch and Lomb refused to bid on periscopes for the S–18 through 41 because the company suffered from limited capacity and considerable current obligations.[15] Of the remaining firms only Kollmorgen and Keuffel and Esser possessed the technical competence.

Unfortunately for Electric Boat, a lower price represented the only satisfactory feature of the Keuffel and Esser instruments. L. Y. Spear, Vice President of EB, argued that Keuffel and Esser's designs would require a revision of the S-class specifications to accommodate a larger periscope head. He also questioned the method employed by Keuffel and Esser to insure the tightness and integrity of the periscope and reminded the Navy of that firm's history of late delivery.

Although the Keuffel and Esser price fell $92,400 below that of Kollmorgen, the latter could produce instruments of much higher quality. Kollmorgen's periscopes not only complemented the S-class design but also employed the higher quality French optical glass. Production finally began in 1918 when the Navy chose Kollmorgen and approved the bid of EB's frequent business partner, General Ordnance, to manufacture the steel tubes to house the periscope optical sets.[16]

In this case, however, the Navy had to do more than simply award the contract. Although Kollmorgen wanted the contract to fabricate optical equipment for the S–18 through 41, it needed assistance from the Navy. Besides its obligations regarding the S-class submarines, the company also had contracts with EB and the Army. Its facilities and equipment were not sufficient to satisfy all of these commitments.

When Kollmorgen asked for $60,000 for new equipment purchases in order to fulfill the Navy's periscope orders, the Navy Department conducted an evaluation of the company. Navy Assistant Paymaster C. D. Fairweather determined that Kollmorgen's financial and management practices did not compare with its technical expertise. Visiting Kollmorgen's Brooklyn plant, he observed that the "records of the company are in most unsatisfactory condition, no cost or factory records being kept." He concluded that Kollmorgen could not meet the periscope contracts for the S class if the Navy refused assistance. Fairweather estimated that the situation required an immediate advance of at least $50,000, and more in the future.[17]

The Navy granted Kollmorgen the money it requested, but, on the advice of the paymaster's office, took direct control in its relationship with the

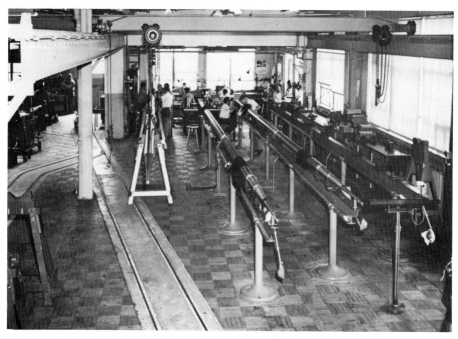

National Archives, Bureau of Ships (RG 19).

Interior of the periscope shop at Kollmorgen Optical Corporation, Long Island City, New York.

company. Instead of allowing EB to act as principal, the Navy Department changed the contract and listed periscopes among those parts that the prime contractor would receive from government sources. This decision gave the Navy greater authority over the procurement process as well as the 10 percent profit EB was to have received for securing the periscopes from a private firm. In spite of an appeal to the Compensation Board that lasted from 1918 to 1920, EB never recovered the money it lost in this redefinition of the Navy's connection with Kollmorgen.[18]

Both the Navy and industry suffered from a shortage of practical experience with periscope technology. Bausch and Lomb, Keuffel and Esser, Kollmorgen, and General Ordnance had little difficulty with the optical theory or the design and manufacture of the lens or the copper and steel tubes. But the novelty of the working periscope, its assembly, and its behavior in a submarine presented problems never before confronted.

Periscopes in the R-class boats, for example, suffered from poor focus, lack of eye buffers on the ocular or eyepiece, low power, and a tendency for air bubbles and moisture to leak into the inner tube of the instrument. Submarine officers frequently—and graphically—described lens scratches, leaks, missing screws, and hydrodynamically induced vibration at normal submerged speeds.[19]

In part, these problems emerged because wartime needs left little time for painstaking trials. Under these conditions, contractors like Kollmorgen had no time to define and solve unanticipated technical obstacles before the operational forces discovered the inevitable flaws that plague any new system.

If the demands of war rendered the flaws more apparent, they also provided a ready means to determine the precise nature of their source. Accelerated production after 1916 placed more submarines at the disposal of the Navy and the private sector, and trial and performance data from these vessels provided the Navy and the optical firms with valuable information on the most pressing problems and possible solutions.

Periscope extension presented a major difficulty to the submarine commanders. In the early S boats all three periscopes often proved too short. During the second round of preliminary trials for the S–3 (SS–107) in June 1920, the submarine had to come far too close to the surface to use the periscope. The first two instruments, measuring 42 and 102 inches respectively, required the conning tower to break the surface or to come precariously close to doing so. The Board of Inspection and Survey team at the trial suggested lengthening the installation to allow the S–3 to run at least ten feet deeper at periscope depth.[20]

American optical science improved this situation over the next decade in spite of minimal national concern with submarine research and development. Research was maintained mainly through the interest of the private sector

NH 89733

A periscope on board S–45 is in the raised viewing position.

in the commercial applications of optical instruments. By 1929 American submarines employed periscopes with optical lengths of at least 27 feet. The Navy installed this type in the O and R classes still in use, as well as in the S–2. Thirty- and 34-foot models became standard in the rest of the S class and the V–1 through 6.[21]

Periscope vibration also emerged as a primary concern. A fully extended periscope often displayed critical vibration as the submarine's submerged speed increased. By the end of the First World War this condition made many periscopes useless at higher underwater speeds. In the preliminary trial of the S–50 (SS–161) in 1922 the periscopes performed well at a submerged speed of 5.99 knots, but vibrated excessively by 6.91 knots. In boats designed to approach 9 knots submerged, this condition represented a significant handicap.[22]

Four years later the Navy and Kollmorgen still confronted this obstacle. During the official trials of the V–1 in 1926 the vessel managed to reach 7.5 knots before its number one periscope experienced critical vibration. Periscope number three absorbed 7.3 knots, but number two managed only 5.65. The Navy had determined by this time that the instrument's structural supports posed the most important problem. The drag on a fully extended scope proved too much for the supports and bearings. Thus, while Kollmorgen instruments performed well optically, the inadequate support system within the hull reduced their operational value.[23]

This situation continued into the 1930s. Electric Boat did manage to sufficiently strengthen the foundation for the control room periscope on *Cuttlefish*, but this secured vibration-free performance only up to 6 knots submerged. The conning tower instrument began vibrating at 3 knots!

The location and size of the two periscopes presented different challenges. The control room device had a diameter of 6 inches, and the conning tower model measured 7 1/2 inches. The latter already had less support within the hull because of its situation. Its greater diameter, which offered greater resistance, precipitated vibration sooner. Unfortunately, even with increased operational testing, engineering offered no lasting solutions before the Second World War.[24]

Habitability

During the Great War the submarine's theater of operations lay in the waters surrounding Great Britain and the European continent. Once the American boats arrived in Europe, their patrol duties kept them at sea for relatively short periods of time. The distances back to Bantry Bay or the Azores for rest, provisions, and repairs did not make habitability an absolutely critical element in a submariner's life.

After the war the shift from the Atlantic to the Pacific as the submarine's primary operational area radically changed the situation. Instead of relatively short trips between home port and the operational areas, the distances traversed by the S-class submarines between the West Coast of the United States and Pearl Harbor exceeded 2000 miles. Boats assigned to the Asiatic Fleet would have to travel another 5000 miles. The size of the S-class vessels and the new distances involved magnified the problems associated with living on board. Since major mechanical failures also plagued the S class, these transpacific migrations took place too often for the officers and crews.

The major environmental problems on board a submarine were as predictable as they were potentially debilitating. In a vessel of approximately 900 tons in which machinery, weapons, and support systems took up most of the room, how could the Navy comfortably accommodate crews of twenty to forty men? Even a technically excellent submarine would not perform up to expectation without a rested and alert crew. Uncontrolled carbon dioxide accumulation alone could significantly reduce the quality of the crew's performance in a critical situation. This danger was compounded by the accretion of food and personal odors as well as by the periodic discharge of potentially dangerous hydrogen from the storage batteries. Therefore, habitability became easily as important a problem as defective diesel engines, periscope vibration, and temperamental torpedo shutters.

Arranging the interior of the boat to allow the crew some comfort on long Pacific voyages became an important issue during the interwar period. In June 1923 Commander Submarine Division 3, Captain Ernest King, argued for an improved interior arrangement so that the burden of constantly living on board would not diminish the effectiveness of the crew.[25] In a letter to BUC&R he argued that it "would appear that the present arrangements for living on board were installed with the idea that living on board was to be intermittent, e.g. only while underway."[26]

Submarine accommodations could no longer reflect just temporary habitation. King suggested moving the wardroom and the crew's head to other locations to make room for additional berths and a shower. To a submariner confined in an S-class boat, the separation of eating, sleeping, and sanitary facilities was critical. Additional heating and ventilation, lockers, and storage facilities also became necessary. King supported Commander Submarine Divisions, Atlantic Fleet, who wrote in February 1923: "There is no question that our submarines are deficient in the many details that make for comfort and contentment and should be improved in this respect. Consideration must be given to every recommendation regarding increased habitability. . . ."[27]

The consensus on strategy and design within the Navy between 1927 and 1936 established a standard displacement of 1450–1500 tons. Although vessels of this size did not present the problems faced by King with the S class in 1923, neither these new submarines nor the mammoth 2000-ton early V-class boats ever completely satisfied the pressing need for more crew space.

As the eternal search for more effective living arrangements continued, the Navy and the private sector also addressed the problem of the stale and sometimes dangerous atmosphere on board American submarines. Each crew member released one cubic foot of carbon dioxide (CO_2) into the boat's environment each hour. During wartime patrols in European waters, the Navy discovered that accumulated carbon dioxide could significantly impair the efficiency of the crew. Beginning in 1917 the General Board held hearings to determine the best method of keeping the air inside the vessel as fresh as possible.

The submarine community drew on the experience of other naval powers and the domestic mining industry for an answer to the carbon dioxide problem. The work of William E. Gibbs of the Bureau of Mines demonstrated the effectiveness of a carbon dioxide absorption system first developed in Great Britain by Dr. J. S. Haldane. Haldane used a soda-lime compound employing lime slaked with a 5 percent solution of sodium hydrate. Slaking combined the soda-lime with water or moist air. Gibbs had found this substance very effective in improving the atmosphere for mine workers by consuming the excess carbon dioxide.

With the help of the Army's Chemical Warfare Service and the facilities of American University in Washington, D.C., the Navy refined a more effective type of soda-lime. The final product emerged from a collaboration between Gibbs, Major R. E. Wilson of the Army's Chemical Warfare Service, and Dr. DuBois of the U.S. Naval Reserve, and soda-lime became the standard agent for absorbing carbon dioxide within American submarines.

Although this method certainly showed promise, it generated some ancillary difficulties. In testimony before the General Board in November 1917, Commander Emory Land of the Submarine Standardization Board discussed the soda-lime canister device developed by the American Can Company. The device drew air across the exposed soda lime by means of a small intake fan. Although this device worked much better than the soda-lime Draeger apparatus used on German U-boats, two of the Gibbs units would add an extra ton to vessel displacement. Land therefore suggested using the canisters only on long-range boats, and not on the coastal defense types. The latter did not stay submerged long enough for carbon dioxide to accumulate

NH 79489

Forward view of cramped submarine quarters prior to the First World War.

81

to a debilitating level, and 1400 pounds of soda-lime might render these smaller boats unstable.[28]

As carbon dioxide absorbers came into regular use on the Navy's submarines, heightened awareness of the need for ventilation led to recommendations for improved hull design and duct systems. Operational testing continued, and the experience of officers like Lieutenant Thomas F. O'Brien of the S–19 persuaded the technical bureaus of the necessity of better ventilation. In 1923 O'Brien made a surface cruise from Guantanamo Bay, Cuba, to the Canal Zone in the S–19, with all hatches closed save for that on the conning tower. His rendition of the experience leaves no room for imagination and little doubt of the need for change:

> I have said "slept" but that is not so. I doubt if any man sleeps with a submarine rolling and pitching the way that boat did and with the air below so frightfully poor, in fact, to use a less pleasant but more correct term, so absolutely rotten as it is. Personally, each time I turned in, I lay there in sort of a dull stupor with a headache, a feeling which the crew say they also experience continually and which they aptly term "going into a dope."

O'Brien recommended more hull openings with effective means to close them upon submergence. He believed that a wider hull and fairwater would permit the installation of more vents and air conduits both for the crew and the propulsion machinery. The ventilation of these boats had to improve, O'Brien felt, or any energetic medical officer would put them out of operation until a solution was found.[29]

In 1923 the Chief of Naval Operations placed additional pressure on BUC&R to improve the habitability of the S boats. With fifty under construction, the issue of living conditions on the boats had become critical to the effectiveness of the submarine force as a whole. The CNO observed, as one example, that the internal temperature of the S boats exceeded 100 degrees in the tropics and hovered only a few degrees above freezing in northern waters. No crew could operate efficiently under these conditions. Habitability, particularly with regard to ventilation, had to improve. Conscious of the high cost of a solution that would serve the entire submarine fleet, the CNO suggested thorough testing before implementing any comprehensive solution.[30]

The large number of operational boats available for the collection of data on ventilation and living conditions gave the technical bureaus the practical information they needed to define problems and fashion more effective solutions. The Board of Inspection and Survey reports focused attention on the ventilation problem as it affected the crew in the motor and battery compartments. On the S-class vessels a portion of the crew slept in or near the battery compartment without the benefit of mechanical ventilation. With the accumulation of hydrogen always a problem in the battery areas, these conditions could certainly impair the health of those on board. Further aft in the motor room poor ventilation allowed the temperature to rise so high that fires and overheating in the propulsion system became a possibility. Greater circulation and cooling was imperative.

Ashore, the Bureau of Medicine and Surgery conducted respiration chamber tests on submarine personnel at the Army's Edgewood Arsenal in Maryland to determine the levels of carbon dioxide and oxygen at which crews could safely work. The experiments concentrated on two major questions. The bureau wanted to know the maximum length of time a submarine could safely remain submerged and the degree of efficiency the Navy could expect from a crew during such an experience.

This research and the practical experiences of the fleet demonstrated that the efficiency of the crew began to fall dramatically as the carbon dioxide level approached 3 percent and the oxygen level declined to 17 percent. If the atmospheric levels of carbon dioxide rose to about 5 percent and the oxygen fell to 10 percent, physical exertion of any sort would become impossible.

By the end of 1927 the Board of Inspection and Survey determined that a submarine crew required a complete renewal of the boat's air every 36 hours. The Bureau of Medicine and Surgery proposed the use of soda-lime devices, more efficient blowers and ducts, air conditioning, and on-board oxygen flasks to insure improved habitability.

In 1927 BUC&R reacted critically to these recommendations. Improved ventilation and the carbon dioxide absorbers became part of the bureau's habitability improvement plans, but BUC&R questioned the necessity of oxygen flasks and air conditioning units because of the premium placed on space.[31] The oxygen flasks never survived the BUC&R objections, but air conditioning fared much better. In spite of the difficulty of limited space, the importance of submarine operations in the Pacific, Caribbean, and South Atlantic led the Navy Department to install an air conditioning system on board *Cuttlefish* in 1935. In the first trials, conducted off Perlas Island near Panama, the change in temperature produced a marked increase in crew efficiency. The boat proved more comfortable, and the quality of the internal atmosphere improved.

Later that year, the *Plunger* class (SS–179) received the first regular operational air conditioning systems, units capable of sustaining the improved on-board atmosphere for 90-day patrols. Besides cooling, these systems also reduced humidity and filtered the air.[32]

By the mid–1930s the bureaus knew more about habitability and had addressed most of the pressing problems that directly affected the performance of the crew. That is not to say that the bureaus had completely solved problems like hydrogen accumulation, excessive carbon dioxide in the atmosphere, inadequate ventilation, and severely limited crew accommodations. In a small cramped vessel like the submarine such difficulties would never disappear. But the Navy did manage to define most of the habitability challenges. Through its own efforts at the Naval Experimental Station and in cooperation with universities and private industry, the Navy significantly improved the environment of the American submarine in the years before the Second World War.

Observations

Without stable torpedo shutters, well-crafted periscopes, effective communications and detection gear, and a healthy on-board atmosphere, the Navy's submarines could not possibly fulfill their mission. Building large numbers of submarines, especially in production runs as long as those of the S class, provided the Navy and private industry with experience in this facet of naval architecture and engineering, which it sorely lacked before the First World War.

The decision of the Navy Department to become deeply involved in submarine construction as a coordinator and catalyst proved one of its most profitable and significant policies of the 1914–1940 period. In all four major problem areas—armament, communications and detection, periscopes, and habitability—the Navy took the lead. It also coordinated its research projects with those in the private sector and academia. When the technology proved critical to effective operation, the Navy even primed the pump by financing plant expansion and equipment purchases, as in the Kollmorgen case. These and other vital developments permitted American submarine designers and engineers to overcome the limits of wartime technology.

In taking the initiative, the Navy not only improved the state of its own vessels but also achieved an intimacy with the submarine and its systems that enabled the service to guide and monitor more effectively the contract work of the private sector. No longer would companies claim the secrets of submarine design, technology, and construction as their private domain.

5

The Achilles' Heel

There can be no doubt that for submarine engines none of the types that have been created till now are entirely suitable.

—Lieutenant Emory S. Land, 12 January 1914.

The need for dependable submarine diesel propulsion systems provoked a major contest between Electric Boat and the Navy for control of technological development and ship construction. Here again, the Navy emerged from the confrontation as the dominant party in the naval-industrial relationship, and naval officials developed a better understanding of the needs and motivations of the private sector in its interaction with the government.

Unlike the design and strategy debate, the controversy over submarine diesel propulsion involved specific fundamental questions regarding critical speeds, torsional vibration, and metallurgy that probed the limits of American science and technology. These issues did not involve traditions, opinions, or personal preferences, but rather serious deficiencies in areas of scientific understanding that only time and research would remedy. The development of a reliable submarine propulsion system during this period involved intense research, frustration with the limits of American technology, disappointment with the motives and capabilities of the private sector, and the added burden of inadequate congressional funding.

In addressing the technical problems, both the Navy and the private sector confronted the dichotomy between craft and science, between the world of the mechanic and that of the scientist and advanced engineer. The experienced craftsman and engine mechanic, with support from a skilled foundry staff, could acquire the degree of sophistication necessary to build, maintain, and reliably operate a Holland gasoline submarine engine or the relatively simple diesels that powered the small F-class boats.[1] But the complexity of designing and building diesels made a quantum leap when submarines grew to 800 or 1000 tons on the eve of American entry into the war. These larger vessels required 15–21 knots to perform their surface mission. With the introduction of larger and more powerful engines, submarine propulsion problems began to require highly trained engineers, as opposed to craftsmen. Accordingly, the responsibility of the Bureau of Steam Engineering for the design, performance, and integration of submarine propulsion systems moved into the realm of the scientist.

The First World War and the U-boats

With the advent of the Great War, both the Navy and its private contractors

NH 68981

K–6 (SS–37), built at Fore River Shipbuilding Company in Quincy, Massachusetts, was one of the first submarines of its class to experience cracked diesel engine castings.

began to experience major difficulties with submarine diesels. In the H-class vessels, built by Electric Boat at Union Iron Works in San Francisco and by the Moran Company in Seattle, BUENG discovered that air compressors and lubrication oil pumps were unable to withstand the engine's intense vibration at high speeds.[2]

Initially the Board of Inspection and Survey attributed these flaws to poor workmanship and put pressure on the contractors to improve their performance.[3] But, even with greater attention to engine quality, the casualties only multiplied and incapacitated an ever-increasing number of boats. Investigating a cracked engine housing on the K–1 in September 1916, the vessel's commanding officer, Lieutenant George L. Dickson, suggested that "the cracks in the housing are due to light construction, unreliability of the two-stroke cycle engines, shafting out of line, and poor governing."[4] This analysis offered the possibility that the problems plaguing BUENG submarine machinery went deeper than poor workmanship.[5]

Lieutenant Dickson's low opinion of the two-stroke diesel cycle was significant in view of the fact that Sulzer Brothers, Ltd., had perfected a reliable engine of this type ten years earlier. Thus it was not the technology, but only its application to submarines that was relatively new and perhaps not fully understood by American naval and civilian engineers. Electric Boat's misaligned shafting and poor governing offered an illustration of America's relative inexperience in submarine diesel construction and installation.

Perhaps the most telling aspect of Dickson's analysis involved the light construction of the engine castings. Cracks in the K-class engines occurred both on the K–1 (SS–32) and K–6 (SS–37). An examination of the casualties to his own boat and others led Dickson to conclude that the metal employed in the K-class, two-stroke engines developed by Nelseco could not withstand the higher temperatures and pressures encountered in standard operation.[6]

Rear Admiral Robert Griffin, Chief of BUENG, shared Dickson's suspicion that the current state of American metallurgy contributed to the flaws in the Navy's submarine diesels. Noting that pressure and temperature caused most of the engine failures, he questioned whether any American metal or alloy could withstand the pressures of 1350 pounds per square inch (psi) and temperatures of 2230 degrees Fahrenheit required of a submarine diesel.[7] When asked by the General Board in October 1916 for his opinion on the engine problem, Naval Constructor Herbert Howard testified in support of Griffin's viewpoint that, compared to Europe, our "trouble is mostly metallurgy. We have not had to make the extensive experiments they have going into the different qualities of steel."[8] After an unsuccessful six-year quest for a commercial firm that could improve the quality of steel castings for submarine diesels, BUENG decided in 1922 to give the job to the

Rear Admiral Robert S. Griffin,
Chief of the Bureau of Engineering,
1913–1921.

NH 60871

Philadelphia Navy Yard. This facility had experience with the main engine castings for the S–10 through 13, and later won the contract for the engines slated for the V–1 through 3.[9] Philadelphia continued to produce castings, especially for the Navy's Bu-MAN diesels, until the spring of 1930.[10] At that time the desire for smaller, high-speed diesels led BUENG Chief Rear Admiral Harry E. Yarnell to resort to the better castings produced by the Naval Gun Factory at the Washington Navy Yard.

When the Navy Department and Congress moved to increase submarine production on the eve of the Great War, neither the private sector nor the Navy had reliable diesels to power the new vessels awarded to Portsmouth, EB, and Lake. Even with Rear Admiral Griffin's concerns about metallurgical deficiency and the looming specter of engines heavy enough to withstand the required heat and pressure adding unwanted tonnage, most naval officials did not yet attribute the problems plaguing submarine propulsion to the fundamental backwardness of American science and engineering. Torsional vibration, broken crankshafts, and deafening noise were viewed by naval and private craftsmen as simply poor workmanship or inadequate maintenance.

As America entered the war and the construction of the O, R, AA (T), and S classes accelerated, the Board of Inspection and Survey illustrated the limited appreciation of the diesel noise problem by proposing the use of a newly developed lubrication formula called "crater compound." After this alternative provided only momentary respite from the diesel cacophony, a herringbone transmission gear then emerged as a possible solution to the vibration and noise problems.[11]

The prevailing wisdom optimistically suggested that experimentation and the customary required trials would shortly provide a solution to the dilemma as long as the technical bureaus made sure the degree of workmanship remained high. In response to reports of vibration and shaft breakage from the Inspector of Machinery at Electric Boat, BUENG confidently replied, "that delays due to this trouble have occurred and will continue until the trouble is remedied, and this delay will be shorter as the experiments and trials of the changes in the design are expedited and pushed to completion."[12]

By 1917 the need to produce more submarines to strengthen America's power to wage war against Germany had quickly replaced concerns about diesel performance. Moreover, many decision makers felt certain that BUENG or private industry would soon solve the perceived mechanical problems. This viewpoint led the Bureau of Construction and Repair to focus on producing current engine designs for the O, R, and T classes, as well as the new S-class boats. Thus the diagnosis of the difficulties with American diesels and the impact of mobilization for war led the Navy to produce in quantity propulsion systems that had already demonstrated their unreliability in peacetime.

Since the Navy Department depended completely on the private sector for the construction of submarines and propulsion systems, it carefully monitored the capacity of industry to cope with the demands of war. Responding to a telegram of 14 June 1918 from Secretary Daniels, both Nelseco and Busch-Sulzer, the major diesel engine companies, assured him that they could continue to provide the quantity needed to power the Navy's submarines over the next year. As soon as it completed the work on hand, Nelseco guaranteed that it could provide the plant space and skilled labor force to mass-produce the four-cycle, 600-horsepower (at 380 rpm) engines slated for use in the S–18 through 41. Other types of fully developed diesels available from Nelseco included the 700-horsepower (350 rpm), four-cycle design installed in the S–3 at Portsmouth and the smaller engines designed for the R, O, H, K, and N classes. Nelseco also declared itself ready to expand its facilities as the demands of war required. However, the firm reminded the Secretary of the Navy that increased production would require such a commitment to plant expansion and new labor that the company would need a start-up time of five months and delivery dates extending beyond a year.[13]

Responding to the same telegram from Daniels, Busch-Sulzer's Vice President and General Manager, James R. Harris, also declared his firm's willingness to accelerate production for the war. He took great pains to communicate to Daniels the production potential of his St. Louis plant and its ability to build two- and four-cycle submarine diesels ranging from 300 to 900 horsepower. On 25 June, Harris journeyed to Washington, D.C., for a meeting at the Navy Department to outline Busch-Sulzer's role in diesel production for the war. Although his firm received a contract on 6 August 1918 for eight pairs of engines to power S-class boats, Harris never tired of reminding the department that his skilled work force needed prompt action and a steady flow of orders to remain constructively occupied and avoid layoffs.[14]

Like Rear Admiral Griffin, many engineers knew American diesel technology did not rank among the best. However, what they had found when German U-boat technology became available after the war made it clear that a huge chasm existed between the state of the art and the engines produced by American manufacturers, especially Nelseco. Shortly after Commander Emory Land testified before the General Board in February 1919 on the necessity of bringing a few German U-boats to the United States, Griffin sent his initial evaluation of German diesel technology to the Secretary of the Navy. With a greater piston speed, more effective oil cooling system, and higher mean effective pressure (mep), the German engines completely outperformed their American counterparts.[15] BUENG's preliminary findings indicated an overall 12 percent greater propulsive efficiency in the German diesels. When the bureau realized that this greater efficiency resulted even when auxiliaries more demanding than those on American submarines drained the power provided by the U-boat main diesels, Griffin concluded that "the results are more than startling."[16]

Before the U-boats actually came to American shores in the fall of 1919, BUENG had acquired two pairs of German diesel engines from the British through Rear Admiral Harry S. Knapp, naval attaché in London and Admiral Sims's successor as Commander U.S. Naval Forces in European Waters. On 15 August, after a short hiatus during which the release of the machinery was approved by the staff of the Paris Peace Conference, the engines arrived for examination and tests at the New York Navy Yard.[17]

Early tests at the navy yard, coupled with the arrival of the U-boats in November, gave the technical bureaus a complete picture of the reliability of the German diesels. They performed consistently well at 450 revolutions per minute (rpm), a speed that usually caused dangerous vibration in the S-class Nelseco machinery. Lieutenant Commander Freeland Daubin, who commanded the U–111 on its transatlantic crossing, drew the attention of the Secretary of the Navy and the technical bureaus to the excellent lubrication system, easy engine accessibility, and the nearly casualty-free trip from Europe.[18] Indeed, the U–111's diesels endured 11,000 miles of testing, at speeds of up to 17 knots with few casualties.[19] BUENG not only put the U–111 diesel through its operational paces but also took the damaged engines from the submarine minelayer UC–97 and managed to produce one good diesel and one good source of spare parts. This machine went to the Engineering Experiment Station at Annapolis for further research.[20]

The Nelseco Controversy

If the best submarines produced by American industry could not measure up to German performance standards, what could the submariners hope for

Official U.S. Navy Photograph, David W. Taylor Research Center

A 1934 aerial view of the Engineering Experiment Station in Annapolis where German diesels underwent testing.

in the future? The extraordinary durability of the German diesels only served to point out the poor quality of the Nelseco engines supplied by Electric Boat for many of the Navy's latest S-class submarines. This realization precipitated a confrontation between the company and the Navy Department that was exacerbated by their inability to agree on the exact nature of the problem plaguing submarine diesels.

Clearly the state of the technology lay at the root of the problem. Torsional vibration was not yet thoroughly understood by the American engineering community.[21] As a result neither BUENG nor EB comprehended the problem well enough to determine precisely the nature and cost of the solution.

In the two years after the Great War, difficulties with Nelseco machinery caused excessive crankshaft cracking as well as cylinder and cylinder head breakage. The vibration of the Nelseco engines too often placed extraordinary stress upon the crankshafts at operational surface speeds. This condition caused severe damage to both the shaft and the engine and frequently sent incapacitated S boats to port for the renewal of pistons, crankshafts, cylinders, engine castings, and cylinder heads or the installation of dampers to retard the vibration.

As a result BUENG required all tachometers to show plainly the rpm ranges that caused destructive vibration and posed the danger of immobilizing the propulsion system. These forbidden ranges were called "critical speeds" or simply "criticals." The bureau faced the possibility of either diminishing, as a safety measure, the power output rating of the engines slated to drive the S class or devising some mechanical means of eliminating or reducing the critical ranges in order to avoid engine failure.

With its technology already three years behind that used on German U-boats in the war, the Navy now found itself faced with commissioning vessels incapable of meeting the performance standards stipulated in their designs. Either BUENG had to adopt re-rated diesels, which could not provide the S-class contract speed, or it had to accept an increase in displacement caused by measures designed to reduce the vibration.[22]

BUENG considered enlarging the diameter of the crankshafts to change their vibration frequency. This would have pushed the critical sectors above or below the rpm required to drive the boat on the surface in accordance with the speed expectations set forth in the contract. Another alternative would have placed vibration absorbers, or dampers, in the engine mountings. Unfortunately, these would have added unwanted tonnage.

Regardless of the preferred approach to the problem, the submariners faced a bleak future. Congress did not place a high priority on submarine research and development, and the Navy and EB did not agree on the nature or the solution of the Nelseco diesel problem.

This episode was not comparable to the development of the American Liberty aircraft engine. J. C. Vincent, chief engineer at Packard Motor Car

Company, and Elbert J. Hall of the Hall-Scott Motor Company, drafted the preliminary specifications for this power plant during a meeting at the Willard Hotel in Washington, D.C., on 29 May 1917. The first production engine was delivered six months later.

The similarity of this engine to state-of-the-art automobile engines greatly facilitated cooperation between the War Production Board, the Navy, Army, and private industry in its development and production. Private industry promptly manufactured four-, six-, eight-, and twelve-cylinder versions because of the familiar technology, the availability of proper tools, and a work force already armed with valuable skills and experience. Few of these advantages existed in the small American submarine market. Thus naval flying boats, such as the HS–1 and the NC–3, benefitted from a situation that proved impossible to replicate for submarine diesels.[23]

The unhappy performance of the S–1 (SS–105) diesel offers a genuine sense of the dilemma faced by both Electric Boat and the Navy Department. In a memo addressing the appearance of crankshaft cracks in the engines powering the S–1, the Inspector of Machinery at Groton, Commander Henry C. Dinger, revealed that both casualties eventually resulted in broken shafts. While EB attributed the first to a flaw in the fabrication of the shaft by a subcontractor, the company was "unable to give any explanation for the second failure. . . ."[24] The problem prompted bewildered engineers at EB to investigate the relationship between critical engine speed and crankshaft failure. During the spring of 1919 they experimented with operational boats, such as the S–1, as well as engines mounted on test stands like the machines destined for installation in the S–32. In every one of these tests Electric Boat technicians experienced casualties with clutches, crankshafts, and connecting rods.

The interpretation of these test results indicated that a wide difference of opinion existed between the technical bureaus and EB. From the BUENG perspective expressed in a letter to the Inspector of Machinery on 9 May 1919, "the troubles were due to the high stresses in the crankshafts [stemming from engine performance] which set up a vibration in the shafting causing excessive noise in the gears and resulting in shaft breakage when the vibrations became synchronized."[25]

For the officials at EB it was less a question of determining the factors contributing to the destructive performance of its diesels than one of making the engine work so the company could fulfill the letter of its agreement. EB perceived itself purely as a provider of services under a contract and proved reluctant to investigate the source of the engine problems at any great length. EB's arrangement with the Navy was clearly spelled out in print, and the company did not wish to become involved in what would amount to a prolonged and costly research and development project exploring the poor performance of the Nelseco diesels.

When BUENG built two Nelseco engines at the New York Navy Yard for installation in the S–4 at Portsmouth, the preliminary trial team set up by the Board of Inspection and Survey observed excessive vibration in the starboard diesel. This caused material damage to the engine in spite of the installation of a vibration damper. The latter became oil-soaked during the November 1920 trials and began to smoke. Consequently, the board considered it inadvisable to run the engines in the S–4 at surface speeds in excess of 304 rpm or 12.5 knots. This shaved 3.5 knots off the designed speed for the boat. With this statement the board pinpointed the Navy's quandary. While advising a reduction in speed to insure the safe operation of the S–4, the board fully realized that acceptance of a slower speed on the S boats ultimately diminished their operational value.[26]

The flaws in these engines did not reflect poor workmanship at New London, but rather a fundamental design flaw in the diesel itself. As Commander Submarine Flotilla 3, Captain Thomas Hart noted with his usual bluntness in a summary report on the Nelseco-powered S–1:

> The engines in the S-one are generally so defective that they cannot be made sufficiently reliable by even major alterations but must be wholly re-designed. That, pending re-engining of S-one, the only chance of obtaining useful service from her is to . . . accept whatever full speed is given, at 340 r.p.m., or wherever the severest "critical" begins.

Hart pronounced the S–1 unable to perform the most basic tasks required of submarine divisions.[27]

Relations between the Navy Department and EB began to deteriorate seriously when the company doggedly resisted addressing the fundamental flaws in the Nelseco diesels. At EB's request, BUENG had re-rated the S–42 through 47 engines in a futile attempt to alter the critical sectors so that the boats could reach contract speed without lingering in the destructive vibration ranges. While the bureau still expected these engines to produce 600 brake horsepower (bhp), it approved the change in the rpm requirement from 380 to 345 rpm on 9 April 1920.[28] Confident that the new engine rates would allow the boats to meet Navy specifications and thus fulfill the contracts, EB resisted suggestions from BUENG that stronger, 8-inch crankshafts replace the 7-inch models currently in use.[29]

In response to an earlier request from Electric Boat, BUENG had authorized re-rating the S–1 and S–18 through 41 diesels to 600 bhp at 340 rpm in December 1919. At that time BUENG first suggested using larger shafts to allow the propulsion system to withstand torsional vibration. Now, after re-rating the S–42 through 47 engines without any significant reduction of the vibration problem, BUENG once again suggested that the company abandon its strategy of trying to thread the needle between the critical sectors to insure safe operation of the diesels. From the Navy Department's point of view, EB was treating the symptoms and not the disease. Torsional vibration plagued the Nelseco propulsion systems, and heavier crankshafts would lessen the chance of destructive vibration. For EB, however, agreeing to a change in shaft size would mean admitting the engines suffered from basic design flaws. This it was not yet willing to do.

Consequently, BUENG filed a delinquency report with the Secretary of the Navy on 10 April 1920 accusing Electric Boat of illegal delay in failing to complete the S-class boats on time. BUENG Chief Rear Admiral Griffin argued that EB, like the bureau, fully realized that the Nelseco diesels had failed to approach acceptable standards, and "yet in order to save a moderate amount of expense involved in a partial redesign, they have been delaying action on S–42 to S–47 in the hopes that S–1 and S–18 to 41 would prove sufficiently successful to meet specified requirements." Electric Boat refused to accept any design changes from the bureau and only agreed to the aforementioned engine re-rating, doing so without ever stating its objections to specific bureau design suggestions or making other proposals of its own.[30]

Over the next seven months EB barely managed to get the S–1 through preliminary trials, only to have engine and shaft vibration keep the vessel out of service for 86 of its first 120 days in service. This was an inauspicious beginning to the six-month and ten-day preliminary acceptance period that automatically went into effect after the successful completion of preliminary trials.

The head of the Submarine Section of the CNO's office, Captain George Williams, wrote a memo on 21 September 1920 for the Chief of Naval Operations that betrayed the sense of urgency, frustration, disappointment, and anger felt by many in the Navy toward EB. The S class represented the best the Navy had, and the unreliability, frequent casualties, and poorly designed engines that typified the class made a radical solution both necessary and, in the current environment, very appealing. Williams recommended that a board of inquiry investigate the work done by Electric Boat for the government. Indicative of the rising tide of resentment toward the company, Williams concluded:

> After an experience with the Electric Boat Company dating back to 1910 and covering submarine and torpedo work, with a personal knowledge of their methods of doing business, . . . my personal opinion is that the elimination of the Electric Boat Company from submarine construction would be a source of financial and military profit to the United States.[31]

When Secretary Daniels placed the matter before the General Board on 26 October 1920, the members decided to hear testimony from representatives of EB, including two of the company's vice presidents, G. C. Davison and L. Y. Spear. Confronted with the failure of the engine re-rating to curb the vibration trouble significantly, Davison shifted back to an old argument against BUENG's diagnosis of design flaws. During his testimony on 4 November 1920, Davison asserted that the poor performance of the diesels actually stemmed from substandard materials used in the fabrication of the crankshafts.[32] One month later, Spear followed the same line of argument, offering calculations and diagrams to support the viewpoint that the crack in the S–1's shaft resulted from a defect in the steel and not from any vibration caused by the diesel engine. BUENG then offered counter testimony to support its contention that the Nelseco design caused most of the casualties.[33]

After the General Board decided to support BUENG, Electric Boat made yet another attempt to avoid complying with the bureau's decision to increase the diameter of all S-class crankshafts to 8 inches. In a letter to the Navy Department dated 15 December 1920, EB proposed three plans to satisfy the General Board and the bureaus. The first option outlined a restoration of the original rating for the Nelseco diesels and the installation of 8-inch shafts. The company claimed that this procedure would cost the Navy $98,000 per boat for the S–18 through 41 series and $59,000 for the S–42 through 47. By comparison, the second and third proposals did nothing more than brace the engines, change the propeller pitch, fit new exhaust thermometers, and incorporate a change of design on the cylinder heads and exhaust valves. EB clearly hoped to convince the department to go the cheaper way by pointing out that proposals two and three would cost the Navy no more than $7,750 for the S–18 through 41 and $6,250 for the S–42 through 47.[34]

When the secretary rejected all three proposals, Electric Boat began to prevaricate once again, repeatedly asserting its faith in the ultimate potential of the Nelseco diesels to perform reliably. It reminded the department that "the difficulties which have arisen in connection with this machinery are the direct result of action imposed upon the Department and ourselves by the stress of war. The war emergency required the production of a large number of sets of machinery to an untried design." Since neither BUENG nor EB itself could have foreseen the torsional vibration problem, the company felt that neither party should absorb the blame for the difficulties experienced with these engines. Electric Boat had decided that, if it could not limit its liability for the Nelseco diesels to simply treating the mechanical symptoms created by poor design, it would use the extraordinary circumstances created by mobilization to guarantee the significant profits it hoped to earn from the war.

While Electric Boat tried to escape the Nelseco dilemma, the Navy Department took measures to force the company to comply with BUENG's efforts to make the boats operationally reliable. On 20 November 1920 the department informed EB that it would withhold $40,000 in royalties and $25,000 in bonuses due on the S–30 (SS–135) because of the "distinctly unsatisfactory condition of the main engines of the S–1, to which class submarine S–30 belongs." BUENG and the Secretary of the Navy hoped that this measure would put pressure on EB to admit that design flaws actually caused the vibration in the Nelseco diesels and that the condition could plague the entire class, not just the S–1.[35]

Although EB rejected this act as a violation of the contract, the Navy Department persisted and explored alternatives. In one scenario the technical bureaus would take the boats away from EB and finish them in a naval facility. Mare Island Naval Shipyard in California, for example, was a prime candidate to complete the S boats under construction for EB at Union Iron Works. However, the three- to eight-month delays in transferring and completing the vessels did not endear this alternative to BUENG or the commander of Mare Island.

Reluctant to assume responsibility for the partially completed boats, the Navy Department returned to a financial penalty as the most appealing and promising vehicle. As Commander Guy Davis, Inspector of Machinery at Groton, pointed out, EB still stood to make 32 percent profit just on the S–18 through 41. This figure did not include the company's share of the Nelseco profits, which derived from Groton's 80 percent interest in that company.[36] He suggested that this method would involve a bare minimum of cost to the Navy and produce an immediate effect.

On 12 February 1921 the Navy Department decided to resolve the Nelseco controversy by also withholding the remaining payments on the S–18 through 41. By striking at the company financially, the department hoped to compel an agreement both on the design revisions and the financing required to render the S boats operational.[37] Assistant Secretary of the Navy Gordon Woodbury rejected as excessive the $98,000 price tag placed by EB on the remedial work required by BUENG, and furthermore looked with favor upon the Compensation Board's recommendation to continue withholding $40,000 in patent royalties on the S–30 until the machinery question was resolved.[38]

This action by the Navy Department precipitated a burst of anger from Henry Carse, President of Electric Boat, and set the stage for the final confrontation between the two principals in this drama. On 9 March EB sent the Navy Department a memo carefully outlining its position and rejecting any effort by naval authorities to depart from the company's interpretation of the submarine contracts. EB protested BUENG's decision to revise the Nelseco diesel design and refused to acknowledge any basic design deficiencies. According to Groton the contract did not oblige the company to remedy inferred defects at its own expense, nor did it link the performance of the S–1 to that of any other boats of its class despite similarities in their propulsion machinery. EB rejected the Navy's right to expect any more than 600 horsepower on the test stand and the maximum contract speed at sea during final trials, stating that "the contractor does . . . deny the right of the Department to exact boat speed *in excess of contract guarantees* at the contractor's expense and under the guise of the procurement of reliable engines." Any other requirement impressed EB as a violation of the contract agreement and the company flatly refused to comply.[39]

When the Navy Department officially decided to persist in withholding payments and royalties, Carse threw down the gauntlet, calling the decision to halt royalty payments on the S–30 "a flagrant violation of the contract for the construction of this vessel." After once again repudiating the assertion that the diesels supplied by Nelseco displayed design defects, he defended the company's position that the viewpoint of BUENG on the diesels did not rest on fact and contract requirements but rather on the "mere inference that inherent defects exist in the design of the machinery for this vessel." He concluded by complaining that the financial penalties chosen by the Navy Department would inflict material damage on the company and reduce sacred contract arrangements to "mere scraps of paper."[40]

Following this outburst Carse received a letter on 23 March from Electric Boat's major subcontractor on the S class, Bethlehem Shipbuilding, demanding further payments for the S–18 through 29, S–31 through 41, and S–42 through 47; if not, work would stop within five days. With Carse's support, EB's L. Y. Spear informed the Navy Department that the company could no longer make payments to Bethlehem without remuneration from the department and would, therefore, do nothing to sustain progress on the S-class boats.[41] Rear Admiral Griffin stood his ground. He convinced Secretary of the Navy Edwin Denby that the alterations in propeller pitch suggested earlier by EB as a remedy to the vibration problem would still require the Nelseco engines to operate far too close to the known destructive torsional vibration speeds of 360 to 380 rpm. BUENG argued that the company's actions actually represented a refusal to correct an utterly debilitating condition afflicting the propulsion systems of many S-class vessels.[42] When the secretary chose to support Griffin's position by leaving the financial penalties in place, EB informed the department that work on the S boats would stop as of 9 April.[43]

This stalemate brought the construction of most S-class boats to a halt until Electric Boat and the Navy arrived at a working agreement early in 1922. The Navy Department satisfied EB's desire for stricter interpretation of the contract in return for the company's compliance with BUENG's demand to install 8-inch crankshafts to compensate for the vibrations induced by the Nelseco diesels. In addition, the department insisted upon changing the cost-plus-10-percent-profit contracts for groups of vessels to fixed-price documents for each boat. This change would give naval authorities a better method of clearly defining responsibility and a firm basis for accurate accounting in order to govern both costs and profits. To seal the agreement and promote improved relations, the Navy Department dropped all financial penalties and claims logged against EB before 6 January 1922.[44]

BUENG learned a series of hard lessons from the Nelseco controversy that changed the course of its behavior for the balance of the interwar period. EB taught the Navy Department and the technical bureaus the liabilities of allowing primary contractors to determine the source of the propulsion machinery in submarines. From this point on BUENG showed great interest in generating alternatives to the traditional diesel vendors when appropriations and building programs allowed. The episode also demonstrated that the domestic effort to develop a reliable submarine diesel desperately needed an agency that could set standards, promote research, disseminate the latest foreign technology, and provide a control factor to better evaluate efforts in the private sector.

Not all American diesel technology provoked as much trouble as the Nelseco engines. Compared with EB's handiwork, the eight S-class submarines built by Lake and powered by Busch-Sulzer gave the operational forces relatively little trouble. The standard 6–M–85, six-cylinder engine, supplied by Busch-Sulzer for the Lake S boats, generated 500 brake horsepower at 410 rpm, a much higher rate than the 340 to 350 rpm EB required to push the Nelseco diesels to their contract output of 600 bhp.

Compared to the Electric Boat product, the Busch-Sulzer diesels performed remarkably well; they did not produce the intense torsional vibration in the crankshafts that haunted the Nelseco machinery. The greatest problem with the Busch-Sulzer engines was their tendency to smoke, which the Board of Inspection and Survey often attributed to trouble with the exhaust system or the heat resulting from the high rpm needed for the required 500 horsepower.

Unfortunately for the Navy, the facilities at Lake and the company's difficult financial condition in the years just before the First World War limited the number of contracts the yard could accept. Busch-Sulzer also relied upon foreign engineering and design expertise to a much greater degree than Nelseco. Thus the demand for increased output caused by the war and the need for homespun technology with a minimum of foreign dependence sent the bulk of the technical bureaus' submarine orders to Electric Boat.[45]

The T Class and the Bu-MAN Diesels

The prevailing desire of many major naval strategists to have the submarine operate with the battle fleet gave birth to the T-class design, with its projected high surface speed and improved seakeeping qualities for blue-water missions.[46] Begun in 1916, the T-class design called for 1107 tons and a 20-knot surface speed provided by diesels that generate 1100 horsepower at 375 rpm. By November 1921 the diesels in the T–2 exhibited excessive vibration at the planned surface speed of 20 knots and, in time, the vessel displayed many of the same problems that tormented the S boats.[47]

Because their Nelseco propulsion systems could not supply sufficiently

NH 70768

A MAN diesel engine installed in the S–20, Mare Island, California, 1932.

reliable power, the Navy Department decided to retire Submarine Division 15's three T-class boats by 1925. BUENG concluded that a battle with EB similar to the S-class dispute would not solve the problem afflicting these larger vessels.

When torsional stress caused by Nelseco diesels destroyed the possibility of either the S or T-class submarines ever attaining the standards specified in their design, avoiding a reoccurrence of this disaster took high priority in naval planning, and the Navy finally entered the engine business.

Circumventing Nelseco, the Navy Department gave Busch-Sulzer a contract in 1921 to power the new 2000-ton V–1 through 3 fleet submarines, while trying to encourage the development of a new system in the private sector for the other six boats of this class. Assistant Secretary of the Navy Franklin Roosevelt sent inquiries to the Allis-Chalmers Company, the General Electric Company, and Manitowoc, among others, to encourage new developments in the field.[48] The poor response betrayed the hazards of a limited market for the private contractors as well as the shortage of federal funds to stimulate research and development. In this environment the Navy Department took another course.

In the spring and summer of 1922, the S–10 through 13 received a new diesel system developed by BUENG at the New York Navy Yard as an alternative to the unreliable technology available in the private sector. This was the Navy's version of the successful MAN diesel, which had powered many German U-boats in the First World War. By June 1920 the progress made at the New York Navy Yard on the Bu-MAN engines had already come far enough to prompt Captain Thomas Hart to make a favorable comparison between this new type of machinery and the Nelseco design then troubling the S class. Although the Bu-MAN engine also experienced torsional vibration problems, it did not display the severity that caused endless casualties in the S boats. The engine proved thoroughly reliable in regular performance as well as air-starting and -reversing tests. Although Bu-MAN diesels weighed more and took up greater space, they could supply 400 more horsepower than the Nelseco engines with an increase of only 100 rpms. If overloaded, these new engines could double the power obtained from the Nelseco product. This substantial increase in reliability and performance offered the Navy the hope of a dependable alternative for fleet submarine propulsion during the last year of the S-class diesel controversy.[49]

The fundamental technology employed in this engine plan came from MAN in Augsburg, which exported its designs and engines all over the world during the interwar period. Companies like Mitsubishi in Japan, Vilanova in Spain, and H. Stinnes in Sweden used submarine diesels either built by MAN or based on its designs.[50] In addition to the U-boats examined by the technical bureaus after the war, BUENG purchased from the British the MAN diesel slated for installation in the U–127 by the Krupp-Germania Shipyard in Kiel during the war. Its superiority was not lost on a Navy doing battle with Electric Boat over utterly unreliable engines. According to the head of the CNO's Submarine Section, Captain Williams:

> The engine has almost the flexibility of a steam engine, can be run at any speed between 40 revolutions and 380, with all conditions of load from 0 to 1850 Brake H. P., started on air, stopped on air almost instantly by distant control, and easily reversible. Its weight per H.P. is 60 pounds. It is so far superior to engines of the Nelseco type now being installed in our new submarines of the Electric Boat Company's design as to render a comparison ridiculous. Should we have available a gun of a new character as superior to our present installation of guns as this design of engine is superior to our present installation of Diesel engines in the Electric Boat Company's boats, we would, as a matter of course, scrap the old batteries. . . . Information from abroad indicates that the Japanese are buying and building engines of this type.[51]

The promise of this kind of quality, the foreign interest in these designs, and the satisfactory progress made on the MAN diesel all led the Navy Department to finance the research and development effort at the New York Navy Yard. A high degree of craftsmanship and mechanical ability would no longer suffice. It was hoped that substantial Navy support would attract the talent necessary to advance the yard's inquiries into the complex scientific and engineering problems on the leading edge of diesel propulsion technology. Besides experimenting with German-made MAN engines, the New York Navy Yard staff also built eight Bu-MAN diesels scheduled for trials in the S–10 through 13 during 1922. Recognizing the American deficiency in materials and manufacturing methods, the New York Navy Yard staff also made a commitment to research in metallurgy, foundry practices, and centrifugal castings. This research helped BUENG place a prototype Bu-MAN in the S–10 by December 1922.[52]

The Commandant of the New York Navy Yard, Captain Charles T. Vogelgesang, pronounced the Bu-MAN engines a success and suggested that BUENG re-engine the M–1 and the L-, S-, and T-class vessels with these new power plants.[53] BUENG satisfied itself for the moment with the S–10 through 13 installation and ran performance and endurance tests in December 1922 to see how the new engines in the S–10 compared to the German diesels in the U–111.

The results indicated both an improvement over Nelseco performance and the persistence of old problems. The S–10 diesel delivered the power the bureau expected, but exhibited casualties reminiscent of the cracked engine castings in the K–1. Both main engines occasionally failed due to air

An aft view of the Bu-MAN diesels in the V-class *Dolphin* (SS–169), 1932.

compressor trouble. The difficulty did not stem from mechanical flaws, but rather from materials that could not withstand the pressure. The compressor cylinders and piston rings either disintegrated or lost their shape when exposed to the stress of normal operation. In his report to the CNO the commanding officer of the S–10, Lieutenant Commander Carroll Q. Wright, stated that some of the cylinders had taken on an elliptical shape while others displayed considerable scoring at the top. Many of the piston rings simply froze in place.

Even with the air compressor casualties the Bu-MAN engines brought the Navy closer than ever to duplicating the enviable performance of the wartime MAN diesels. Although not as severe as those pestering the Nelseco diesels, the Bu-MAN machinery did have its own critical vibration sectors, leading BUENG in 1922 to require all tachometers to provide the proper indicators for the safe operation of the vessel. Unlike the Nelseco diesels, however, the torsional tests conducted on the Bu-MANs revealed a vibration range close to that of the German U-boats. The major critical sectors occurred between 225–235, 320–360, and above 425 rpm. The first sector was mild, the second violent, and the third occurred beyond the authorized operating range for the S–10. Unlike the earlier effort to find a safe operating range between the many dangerous sectors characteristic of the Nelseco engines, only the middle range of 320–360 rpm posed a potential problem.[54]

This clone of the wartime MAN diesel certainly offered promise for the future, but the New York Navy Yard still had a long way to go. The engines gave Lieutenant Commander Wright 300 hours of reliable service and promised more if the technical bureaus could find materials better able to withstand operational stress. But the S–10 was only the U.S. Navy's first step in closing the gap between German and American diesel technology. Mindful of that, Wright reminded the CNO that the U–111 diesels, equipped with the same piston rings the engine had on its transatlantic crossing in 1919, still operated reliably for Portsmouth three years later.[55] From this point on, the Navy Department would have to rely on scientific research and development to make the Bu-MAN the reliable source of power the submarine fleet desperately needed.

The technology gap diminished with the Bu-MAN, but it did not disappear. Even if the new engine performed well mechanically and the technical bureaus found stronger materials, its proportions still presented a problem to the submarine community. Speed characteristics set by the General Board now called for a surface speed of approximately 12 to 15 knots. Bu-MAN engines large enough to achieve these speeds would, by their size alone, severely compromise the habitability of any 800-ton vessel like those of the S class. While the controversy over the submarine's role and the size of future designs raged at full tilt during this period, many within the Navy, like BUENG Chief Rear Admiral John K. Robison, did not believe the S class could reconcile the need for ample crew space for long patrols with the need for an engine of the size required to provide the speed mandated by the General Board. Here the technology and the strictly defined expanse of an S-class submarine presented an impossible conflict.[56]

The Bu-MAN engines seemed better suited to the larger V class. To explore the possibilities of powering the much larger V–5 and V–6 with the New York Navy Yard diesels, BUENG recalled the T–3 from the mothball fleet at Norfolk in December 1924 to serve as a 1107-ton test vessel for the Bu-MAN engines. The Navy Department secured $600,000 in congressional support for the venture and set aside one year for installation and preliminary testing. After a short delay, the T–3 finally went to sea powered by its new machinery in January 1926.[57]

Test results indicated that the expectations of many within the Navy had clearly outstripped American technology. The size and weight of the engines necessary to secure the 21-knot performance required of the V boats would entail a major redesign of their hull. Materials presented the most telling problem. Even with the efforts of the Philadelphia Navy Yard, BUENG could not procure sufficiently durable thin-section steel castings. Private foundries would not guarantee that the lighter weight the bureau wanted would stand up to the stress of diesel operation. Therefore the New York Navy Yard's Bu-MAN engines weighed 10 percent more than the German-built MAN engines that BUENG had installed in the S–14 through 17 for purposes of comparison.[58] Representing BUENG before the General Board in December 1927, Captain Ormond L. Cox testified:

> The thin section steel castings we have not been able to duplicate in this country. There are certain things in this country that we have not been able to equal German practice. Probably in time we will. At the present time nobody in this country can do it for our engines. Therefore, the New York Engine [Bu-MAN] will be heavier because we have to put in more material, make thicker sections to insure that we will get a fairly good casting.[59]

Both the technical bureaus and Busch-Sulzer faced a long period of intense materials research before American diesels could provide the power necessary to drive the V-class submarines reliably without adding prohibitive tonnage or destroying a boat's habitability. As a consequence, Busch-Sulzer chose to make the V–1 through 3 submarine diesel contract the last it ever sought from the United States Navy. The limited market and the small amount of available work during the 1920s made the investment required to take the next step in development far too expensive.

Keeping Pace with Technology

In 1930, when the Navy Department finally settled on a 1110-ton design for the V–8 and V–9, BUENG decided on MAN propulsion for these boats, either purchased abroad or provided by the New York Navy Yard. Prompted

Rear Admiral Harry E. Yarnell,
Chief of the Bureau of
Engineering, 1928–1932, kept the
Navy abreast of diesel propulsion
technology by initiating contacts
with MAN in Augsburg, Germany,
in 1930.

NH 728

by the unsettled political atmosphere of Depression-era Weimar Germany, BUENG asked the Judge Advocate General to explore article 192 of the Versailles Treaty for any prohibition against foreign purchases by the Navy, specifically those from Germany. The Judge Advocate General insisted that the treaty did not forbid the purchases as long as the Navy did not deal with Germany directly.[60]

The Navy's caution was out of concern that the Japanese had violated the spirit, if not the letter, of the Versailles Peace accords by importing not only MAN diesels and designs but also German technicians as teachers and maintenance personnel. To comply with the requirements of the treaty but still benefit from the expertise in Augsburg, the Navy decided to deal with MAN via its Swiss subsidiary, Rauschenbach.

In spite of political instability and the obvious danger of relying on a foreign power for weapons technology, BUENG under Rear Admiral Harry Yarnell concluded that the bureau needed a relationship with Augsburg. Wartime MAN technology had spawned the Bu-MAN design and stood for all that seemed reliable and modern in diesel propulsion. BUENG wanted the latest products of German research and development in order to upgrade the Bu-MANs and refine its knowledge and skill.

MAN had approached the Navy Department twice in the first half of 1930 with offers to sell outright or to license the New York Navy Yard to manufacture either a 700-rpm, lightweight engine or the 480-rpm, four-cycle, single-acting diesel. At a remarkable 28 pounds per horsepower, BUENG called the latter "the very highest development anywhere of submarine engines."[61] Intensely interested, Rear Admiral Yarnell visited MAN in Augsburg and remained for three months discussing the Navy's needs and studying the latest in MAN technology.[62]

This pursuit of German technology disconcerted the members of Congress responsible for naval appropriations. Yarnell went before the House Committee on Naval Affairs on 12 January 1931 to argue for funds to both expand diesel research and development at the New York Navy Yard and purchase German diesels for examination by BUENG. As was predictable, some members of the committee wanted the money earmarked for purchases abroad spent on domestic engines. To the arguments made by James McClintic (D–Oklahoma) and A. Piatt Andrew (R–Massachusetts) suggesting that the Navy had not yet exhausted the capabilities of the American diesel industry, Yarnell responded:

> The Bureau of Engineering is in close touch with all diesel engine manufacturers; but as I stated, our naval requirements are different from land or merchant marine requirements. None of the companies is able to expend the money necessary for experimentation for a naval engine especially when the market for the product is rather limited and uncertain.[63]

Yarnell's effort brought BUENG $3 million for submarine diesel R&D as well as an additional $500,000 for purchases abroad. The bureau intended to use the smaller sum to acquire MAN's latest engine models, and the balance of the admiral's research and development appropriation went into the Navy's own program at the New York Navy Yard.[64]

Rear Admiral Yarnell went before the Committee on Naval Affairs well briefed by his bureau on current domestic and international diesel technology for submarines. The New York Navy Yard and Electric Boat monopolized domestic research and development in this field. The New York Navy Yard worked to refine its Bu-MAN, which had evolved from the MAN 1915 diesel. During the interwar period, EB experimented with a high-speed, double-acting, two-cycle engine; an opposed-piston, two-cycle crankless engine; and the application of supercharging to four-cycle, single-acting machines.

Beyond America's borders, BUENG explored the diesel engines developed in Great Britain, Italy, Denmark, Switzerland, France, and Holland for the best possible alternatives for American submarines. Of all the private contractors involved, only Vickers in Britain and MAN in Germany had substantially improved upon their wartime designs, having adopted mechanical fuel injection over air injection. However, none of the companies investigated by BUENG in the decade after the war had achieved advances in light, high-power diesels comparable to those attained by MAN in 1915.[65] Thus Yarnell pursued an agreement with MAN to grant BUENG continuing access to this German technology.[66]

It was his complete knowledge of the international diesel situation and first-hand experience that had originally prompted Yarnell to ask Congress for the $3.5 million increase in BUENG's budget. He felt confident that, equipped with the proper financial support, German ideas and hardware could place the Navy in an advantageous position and stimulate the domestic diesel industry with the infusion of new ideas. In the environment created by the Great Depression and the long dry spell for the submarine contractors, BUENG affirmed that

> there are great sales possibilities in this country in all fields because these new types [of diesels] are now applicable to other uses. . . . It is, therefore, possible to interest commercial firms in the manufacture of high speed, light weight diesel engines for all naval purposes, and thus profit by past errors and handicaps.

The Navy could simultaneously create new jobs, especially in the railroad-support industries emerging with the development of diesel locomotives; encourage private-sector participation; promote a much more stable market; and supply the submariners with a reliable diesel engine.[67]

After Yarnell's return from Europe in the summer of 1930, Herr Hausenblas, a representative of the MAN board of directors, came to Washington. When he re-proposed a $2.5-million licensing agreement that the company had first advanced in a February meeting at the bureau, Yarnell countered with an offer that the Germans found interesting. BUENG proposed an arrangement by which the Navy would pay royalties on individual engines built at the New York Navy Yard from Augsburg's plans. Yarnell specified the WV 28/38 (1500 horsepower) and the MV 40/46 (2000 horsepower) as the diesels for which the Navy would pay royalties according to the horsepower rating of the engine. Thus if in the future a new model or variation provided additional power, the Navy Department would have the option to build it, but at a price determined by the increased output. This proposition laid the foundation for an agreement with MAN signed on 25 February 1931.[68]

This concordance gave BUENG the freedom to rely on MAN's experience and expertise. With this foundation the New York Navy Yard further developed the Bu-MAN, especially since Augsburg now employed cast iron for its engine castings, which provided a welcome respite from perennial American metallurgical difficulties.[69]

Unlike the situation in the immediate postwar years, the deal with MAN demonstrated that BUENG had wrested the initiative from the private sector and provided leadership and direction not only for its own research and development effort at the New York Navy Yard but also for private industry. When Electric Boat acquired a special license to build two M(9)V 40/46 MAN diesels on 21 April 1932, BUENG's familiarity with the technology assured a better installation in the *Cuttlefish* and more reliable performance.[70] Private industry also benefitted from the Navy's knowledge of MAN fuel-injection techniques and its research into two- and four-cycle engines for use in both submarines and surface craft.

Electric Propulsion

To complement the agreement with MAN and augment its role as a leader in naval technology, BUENG explored an alternative that would eliminate torsional vibration in its diesels and draw more private-sector contractors into the submarine market. Traditional submarine surface propulsion linked both diesels and electric motors directly to the propeller shaft in a system known as diesel direct drive (DDD).[71] This configuration conducted the motive power and destructive vibration to the propellers. Now the bureau seriously considered using electric power. Appearing for the first time in 1924 to power the 2000-ton V–1, diesel electric drive (DED) did not join the diesel engines directly to the shafts or require the long and frequently too elastic propeller shafts necessary in DDD systems.[72] Thus the primary cause of misalignment would disappear along with nearly all of the criticals. Furthermore, DED offered the possibility of providing additional speed to that provided by a traditional drive system. Similar research and development work on electric drive by the railroad industry also promised greater involvement by the private sector.

For all its advantages, however, experience with diesel electric drive in the early V class made lightweight diesel engines absolutely necessary. The few tons they conserved would compensate for the heavy electrical machinery required to achieve the 17-knot surface speed specified for *Porpoise* and *Pike*. Many of the naval engineers preferred to replace the two large diesels mounted parallel to one another in the direct drive arrangement with three or more smaller, lighter machines. With DED, the Bureau of Engineering might sidestep the destructive vibration that frustrated the Nelseco engines, but the problem of materials and weight would persist.

In 1928 the Navy first investigated diesel electric drive in the four boats of Submarine Division 18. BUENG had re-engined the S–14 through 17 with MAN diesels directly from Germany and sent them down to the submarine base at Coco Solo in the Canal Zone to test the performance of DED in a tropical climate. Early indications showed that running under diesel-electric power on the surface placed great strain on the motors and frequently caused overheating. This situation had occurred during trials performed by the S–14 in February 1928, and the BUENG and the Board of Inspection and Survey needed to know if the high temperatures would prove prohibitive.[73] When the

Board of Inspection and Survey suggested closing the engine room door and drawing all of the ventilation air through the air-induction line leading into the motor room, the better ventilation reduced the temperature of the motor room air and allowed much better performance.[74]

Free to explore the possibilities offered by electric power without the fear of a prolonged development program or debilitating obstacles, naval engineers were converted to the use of DED. If BUENG chose all-electric drive supported by diesel-powered generators, only the motors would actually drive the boat, and the diesels could run at a more efficient, constant speed to provide the required power. This would finally eliminate the torsional vibration problem and wrest more reliable performance from diesels, which would not be directly connected to the shafts. Uncoupling the engines from the shafts also permitted designers to vary the number, size, and arrangement of the diesels in the vessel. This made all-electric just that much more appealing.[75]

The Navy had a host of reliable firms that had served the submarines well for the production of electric motors during the 1914–1940 period. Ridgeway Manufacturing Company, Westinghouse Electric & Manufacturing Company, Diehl Manufacturing Company, General Electric, and EB's subsidiary, Electro-Dynamic, were the major suppliers of this product for a wide variety of civilian and military purposes.

The batteries posed a most difficult problem early in the development of a reliable submerged electrical drive system. Before the First World War, BUENG had difficulty with the storage batteries supplied by the Edison Storage Battery Company. The E–2 (SS–25), fitted with storage batteries manufactured by Edison, experienced an explosion caused by excessive hydrogen accumulation in 1916. Exide and Gould later provided much more reliable storage batteries for the S and V classes. However, the deterioration of the battery casing and the possibility of a short circuit induced by the exposure of the electrical elements to seawater remained a problem throughout the pre-1940 period. Hydrogen accumulation remained a habitability problem and prompted the Navy Department to engage in extensive research into neutralizing the gas by early detection, ventilation on the surface, and chemical means when submerged.[76]

At the end of the first postwar decade, the diesels themselves posed the only obstacle to the use of DED in submarines. Vice President of Electric Boat L. Y. Spear commented to the General Board in July 1929 that the weight of the electric apparatus needed to propel submarines between 1000 and 2000 tons absolutely required a lightweight diesel of high power (325–425 rpm), or the resulting tonnage would make the entire project unfeasible.[77]

The Navy Department quickly recognized the problem and BUENG compiled information on every American firm capable of producing a lightweight diesel that could make all-electric drive viable. After investigating

Nordberg Manufacturing Company, Busch-Sulzer, Winton Engine Corporation, McIntosh & Seymour Corporation, Westinghouse, and Trieber, the bureau concluded that, although the future held great promise, lightweight, high-speed engines were still experimental. To perfect any of the current industrial designs would demand a research and development program of long duration with considerable development and plant costs. In August 1929 BUENG's Admiral Yarnell had to admit that there "is no engine in existence today which is entirely suitable for submarine electric drive," and the bureau expected that any private company undertaking the venture would risk in excess of $4.1 million.[78]

As opposed to official policy during and immediately after the First World War, the Navy Department did not pause and wait for the private sector to supply a suitable engine. BUENG, now under the direction of Rear Admiral Samuel Robinson, initiated a competition to develop "the type of Diesel engine driven generator unit which each particular firm was prepared to build to satisfy the weight and space limitations of the hull used in the latest type of submarines built at that time—*Cachalot* and *Cuttlefish* [V–8 and V–9]." The experience of the Nelseco controversy and the failure of the S- and T-class boats precipitated a change in attitude and practice that resulted in the MAN license and the exploration of electric drive. Robinson intended to continue setting the pace.

Rear Admiral Samuel M. Robinson, Yarnell's successor, initiated a bureau-sponsored competition that drew diesel contractors into the submarine propulsion market.

NH 47178

109

By 1932 BUENG had become well accustomed to playing the catalyst, as this competition illustrates. With a number of companies already anxious to develop successful drive systems to satisfy the growing demand for electric propulsion from the Burlington Railroad and the Union Pacific Railroad, the bureau could not have timed its invitation better. The announcement immediately drew five firms into the race and inspired two others to follow. The Winton Company, founded by diesel engineer and automobile manufacturer Alexander Winton, offered to build a twelve-cylinder, two-cycle engine capable of 950 bhp at 720 rpm. After the company's eight-cylinder model passed tests prescribed by the Engineering Experiment Station in Annapolis, BUENG ordered sixteen Model 201A, sixteen-cylinder engines for the 1933 fiscal year construction program and twelve more for 1934.

The other four initial entries in the competition failed to measure up to bureau standards. Thus, Stearns Mechanical Laboratories, Sun Shipbuilding and Drydock Company, EB, and Continental Motors failed to find a permanent place in the Navy's industrial base for diesel engines.

Two latecomers, however, had greater success and offered Winton, which was absorbed by General Motors in 1930, brisk competition. Fairbanks, Morse & Company (FM) and Hooven, Owens, Rentschler Company (HOR) developed German aircraft and submarine diesels into engines that powered the SS–177 through 180 (FM) and the SS–181 (HOR). The Fairbanks-Morse engine, which received BUENG approval in time for the 1934 construction program, generated 1300 bhp at 720 rpm.[79] Fairbanks-Morse adapted its basic design from the German Junkers Jumo aircraft engine, which commonly appeared in long-range flying boats. The HOR engine introduced yet another MAN design to the Navy. This vendor, boasting links with Augsburg extending back to a licensing agreement of May 1924, proposed a U-boat diesel generating 1300 bhp at 700 rpm.[80]

Initially plagued by a series of difficulties caused by poor materials and welding techniques, by 1938 the GM-Winton Model 16–248 and a more powerful Fairbanks-Morse engine with an improved welded frame would give the Navy a firm foundation for submarine propulsion. The adoption of the hydraulic clutch by BUENG in 1935 and the adaptability of electrical wiring gave designers and engineers the freedom to compose new propulsion arrangements. Now the electric motors and the diesels could occupy different sections of the submarine. These developments also gave birth to a pair of new propulsion system arrangements. The composite system provided the benefits of electric drive with the added advantage of having one diesel linked to the shaft via the reduction gear. The more frequently used alternative was diesel electric reduction drive (DERD). This arrangement, employed in five different variations linked only the electric motors to the reduction gear.[81]

In contrast to the success of GM and FM, the HOR engines in *Pompano* (SS–181) virtually disintegrated as a result of its brittle steel construction.

The company resorted to flame-hardening in order to reduce extraordinary wear and bring the casualties under control. The whole process took nine months, and HOR never recovered its reputation after a barrage of severe criticism from BUENG and the popular press.[82]

Observations

The Nelseco diesel controversy obliged the Navy and industry to identify and address a fundamental problem implicit in their relationship: neither party recognized the extent or nature of its dependence upon the other. Each held a different perception of its responsibility in the development and construction of submarines. The resulting struggle was an important factor in the development of a command technology for submarines in the United States.

Electric Boat's directors preferred a narrow or strict interpretation of their contractual relationship with the Navy Department. This inclination intensified, as the contract seemed the only means of protection against the flood of Navy claims against the company for the poor performance of the Nelseco machinery.

This course, while certainly in step with traditional business practice, was incompatible with the constantly evolving nature of the technology—one that neither EB nor BUENG completely understood. In adhering to this course, Electric Boat threatened to reduce dramatically the operational value of the submarines it produced. The naval authorities could not accept the handicaps that the Nelseco diesels inflicted upon the S and T classes, but any effort to address the diesel problem was interpreted by EB as an effort to obtain something more than the contract promised.

The General Board and the technical bureaus proved just as self-serving. In tackling the fundamental problems plaguing the Nelseco engines, naval authorities viewed the diesel problem as a developmental challenge to the combined resources of the Navy and private industry. They presumed that the companies involved would commit themselves to solving problems like this, even if the effort went beyond the terms of their contractual responsibilities. Those within the Navy charged this viewpoint with a sense of urgency and teamwork characteristic of mobilization and carried it well into the postwar era.

This view displayed both wisdom and naiveté. The facilities and skills at Portsmouth Naval Shipyard and the New York Navy Yard were wisely upgraded to provide both increased capability and welcome competition for EB. But the Navy Department and the technical bureaus unrealistically expected private companies to help create a new generation of dependable diesels using the Nelseco S-class model as a prototype. This policy not only failed to take into account the limitations of private resources, but also asked firms like EB to work beyond the carefully composed terms of their agreement with the Navy.

Evaluated in this context, the intensity and rancor of the clash between Electric Boat and the Navy becomes much more understandable. Naval authorities felt betrayed and disillusioned, and EB was on the defensive, trying to protect its profits and limit its liability.

The Nelseco controversy also demonstrated the need for the Navy to take the initiative in submarine technology. Without knowledge of the latest developments and understanding of their implications, the submarine community would quickly find itself in the same unenviable position it occupied when the diesel controversy began after the Great War. Thus the Navy Department gradually discarded the passive policy of allowing private vendors to determine the propulsion system in Navy submarines and assumed the strong, deeply involved role of catalyst, planner, and director. The initiative of Rear Admirals Yarnell and Robinson resulted in the MAN license, the development of electric drive, and the timely exploitation of the electrical industry and railroad market to the benefit of the Navy's submariners.[83]

6

Conclusions

The Great War provoked worldwide social and political revolution, generated new perceptions of reality, and prompted Western society to revise a fundamentally benign view of technology. In a less profound but nonetheless significant manner, the United States Navy also experienced a metamorphosis. Absolutely dependent upon the private sector at the beginning of the First World War, the Bureau of Construction and Repair and the Bureau of Engineering reached a level of design and construction expertise on the eve of Pearl Harbor equal to that of the Electric Boat Company. By 1940 these developments, combined with the authority to award contracts, placed the Navy Department in a position to control a mature command technology for submarines.

At the beginning of this period conflicting motives, goals, and expectations threatened the development of a working relationship between the Navy and industry. Legal and technical disputes, like the Nelseco controversy, seemed to affirm for the bureaus the purely mercenary nature of the private sector. Had the initiative to provide industry with greater incentives and expert technical guidance not come from the Navy, American submariners might have been forced to settle for the product that any given contractor currently had for sale.

Although the Navy Department and technical bureaus first perceived contractors like Electric Boat and Lake as mercenary firms, the private sector submarine builders had a different image of themselves. They were businessmen with a product to sell, determined to maintain their technological edge. These firms intended to pursue research and development on their own terms and at their own pace, and to profit by selling their results to the Navy. Thus in the first postwar decade, the major partners in submarine construction had not yet developed the carefully defined interdependence that would later make anticipating the Navy's needs a vital part of Electric Boat's business.

Clearly, the peculiar circumstances of mobilization and the postwar naval-industrial relationship brought together two parties with dissimilar viewpoints. The Navy's mission to develop and build warships and industry's desire for profit and growth were certainly legitimate ambitions but, at least at the outset, they were also completely incompatible. To produce a better product, the Navy Department naively expected industry to commit talent and resources beyond the level called for in the provisions of the contract that defined each side's responsibilities. This same kind of myopia led contractors like Electric Boat to believe that the submarine force could settle for vessels with poorly designed engines, terrible habitability, and numerous other defects.

In spite of their conflicting views, the Navy and industry needed one another. Given the experiences and lessons of the Great War, the Navy required operational submarines and the technical cooperation of private industry to supplement efforts at naval research and construction facilities. At the same time, the demise of Simon Lake's firm in 1924 and Electric Boat's struggle to survive the dearth of consistent interwar construction conclusively demonstrated how badly the private sector needed a steady stream of orders from the Navy.

But mutual dependence did not automatically provide the incentive and direction necessary for building submarines and advancing American submarine technology. Naval leaders had to take the initiative in a number of areas during the interwar period. Dissatisfied with industry's early control over the technology and the market, the technical bureaus permitted Lake's demise and utilized available assets to develop Portsmouth into a first-class submarine yard. Naval authorities also played the role of coordinator or catalyst for certain essential technologies, supporting and supplementing work by firms like Kollmorgen on periscopes as well as projects by naval, industrial, and university teams on radio transmission and underwater sound. Accomplishing these tasks during a period of severely limited financial resources made the bureaus more sensitive to the trials of the private sector and provided naval and civilian personnel with an education in naval-industrial relations.

Practical experience gained through study of the German U-boats in the interwar period also proved invaluable. Examining these vessels enabled the technical bureaus and the submarine community to refine American submarine strategy, determine the best design to carry out the intended mission, and improve the service's technical capability. The Germans had developed the submarine far beyond prewar expectations. Their substantial advances in U-boat design, construction, and combat systems dramatically and soberingly illustrated how much the Navy still had to accomplish.

In his letter to the Secretary of the Navy penned in 1921, Captain Yates Stirling, Commandant of the Philadelphia Navy Yard, forcefully pointed out the primitive state of the Navy's submarines. His action sparked a tumultuous design and strategy debate that lasted the decade. The climax of this dispute occurred between 1928 and 1930, when Commander Thomas Withers, commanding officer of Submarine Division 4, with the support of the Naval War College and the Submarine Officers Conference, proposed imitating the offensive strategy and solo tactics employed by the Imperial German Navy during the Great War. Only then did the major authorities within the Navy begin to consider seriously the prospect of independent submarine operations and a vessel design suitable to the task.

These ideas would not capture the entire Navy in the way they did the submarine community for another decade. Even after their ideas did take root, it was often difficult for the submariners to make themselves heard. Future Commander Submarine Force, Pacific Fleet, Charles Lockwood in a letter written to his friend, Commander Francis Low, lamented the scattering of his submarines along a 30- to 40-mile scouting line during exercises such as Fleet Problem 21 in 1940. Restraining the vessels in this fashion deprived them of their greatest value to the fleet—independent offensive action against the enemy. Lockwood concluded by saying, "We learn the same lessons each year and I hope to live to see the day when we will be allowed to profit from them."[1]

The initiative of Withers, the Submarine Officers Conference, and the staff at the Naval War College would eventually make operating independently against enemy forces and inflicting casualties the primary task of American submarines. Gathering intelligence for the fleet remained an important, but secondary mission.

In this involved process of strategic revision and technical change also lay the roots of the unrestricted submarine warfare policy officially adopted against Japan shortly after the attack on Pearl Harbor. American interwar naval planners had judiciously avoided suggesting that the Navy's submarines should attack merchant vessels. They did not want to face the same charges leveled against the Germans after the First World War. But in a national emergency would the naval leadership maintain its reluctance to direct its offensive submarine strategy, fortified now with the newer, more effective submarines developed in the 1930s, against enemy merchant vessels as well as enemy warships? Historian Samuel Flagg Bemis traced the origin of the American unrestricted submarine warfare decision back to 1940, and James E. Talbott has since argued that support for this type of warfare existed within the Navy as far back as 1937.

Actually, the revisionist thinking of the American submarine community in the late 1920s and the designs developed as expressions of these operational views contributed to a favorable environment within the Navy for unrestricted submarine warfare a full decade before Pearl Harbor.[2] For example, the participants in the Navy's interwar Fleet Problems and Naval War College exercises, although limited by international law to attacks on enemy warships and the strict rules of cruiser warfare when attacking merchant vessels, recognized the readiness of potential adversaries to use unrestricted submarine warfare against commerce. In this way, American officers playing the part of the "Orange" or "Red" enemy found themselves planning to defend against a *guerre de course* or to execute a strategy of this type against the United States. During this period, American naval planning for these exercises also evolved from severe restrictions regarding commercial vessels to approved operations against enemy-escorted convoys during Naval

War College Joint Problem No. 1 of 1926 and Fleet Problem No. 13 of 1932. Ideas and experiences such as these laid an early foundation for submarine operations against the Japanese merchant fleet in spite of national policy and international agreements. As is so often the case, the nature of the conflict and the capability of the Navy's submarines, and not detached prewar discussions of proper behavior, determined the degree and manner of commitment.

The American fleet submarine, which so effectively executed this strategy against the Japanese between 1941 and 1945, represented a new synthesis made possible by Stirling's assault on the technical reliability of the S class and Withers's strategic challenge. After these first steps the support and sensitivity of Admirals Wiley, Yarnell, and Robinson proved critical. Wiley, as Commander in Chief, U.S. Fleet, along with the Naval War College staff, permitted Withers's ideas to prosper in a potentially inhospitable environment. Yarnell and Robinson utilized German technology from MAN at a time when America could not afford the extensive diesel research and development program that the submarine force desperately needed.

To these naval leaders, practical experience suggested that the Navy Department should clearly define its goals and take the initiative in its relationship with industry. In this way the construction program could produce the best possible submarines and ensure growth and profit for the private sector. This became the underlying assumption of naval policy toward industry after regular construction resumed in 1931.

New historical research on the economy and industry in Germany and America by historians like Volker Berghahn suggests that the Navy's relationship with MAN and the import of German diesel technology was atypical of the behavior of German and American industry during this period. Importing German diesel technology from MAN to supplement the Navy's research and development program went against the overwhelmingly west-to-east flow of modern industrial innovation in management, production, and technology during the interwar period. In most instances traditionally conservative German industrialists sought, often reluctantly, to imitate American progress in these areas. That the United States Navy had to seek technological expertise abroad demonstrates the isolation of the early interwar submarine market from the mainstream of an otherwise vital and innovative interwar American economy.[3]

The entry of Manitowoc into the submarine market illustrated the Navy's success in establishing its authority over industry in the years before Pearl Harbor. Electric Boat could not resist a Navy Department directive that the company provide Manitowoc with the technical and administrative assistance needed to produce clones of Electric Boat's SS–215. Twenty years earlier the Navy's inferior technical knowledge and junior position in the naval-industrial relationship would have made such a directive impossible.

The sectional hull construction of this *Gato*-class submarine is an example of prefabrication techniques employed by Manitowoc Shipbuilding Company during the early 1940s.

But now the situation had changed so substantially that the Secretary of the Navy and BUC&R could determine the degree of cooperation expected from Electric Boat in every phase of preparing and supporting the new company in its effort to build submarines. Considerable naval investment in expanded Electric Boat facilities at Groton and Bayonne during 1940 provided further incentive for the company to comply with the Navy's wishes.

In the final analysis, the tables had turned completely by 1940. A Navy once utterly dependent upon the private sector for submarine technology and construction now built its own submarines and worked on the cutting edge of a number of vital technologies. The submarine industry, while profiting from its business with the Navy, had indeed, as L. Y. Spear feared, lost much of its independence. The future of private industry's partnership with the Navy would require firms like Electric Boat, Allis-Chalmers, Fairbanks-Morse, and General Motors to produce submarine systems in response to specific naval needs, or in anticipation of them. These developments would serve the Navy well in the next decade.

117

Appendixes

A. Chronology

1888   The French inventor Gustav Zédé designs and builds the electrically powered *Gymnote*.

        Bureau of Construction and Repair design competition brings inventor John P. Holland a contract to build *Plunger*.

1892   Gustav Zédé participates in the creation of a larger version of *Gymnote*, which bears his name.

        Rudolf Diesel invents the diesel engine.

1893   The first model of the diesel engine is manufactured by MAN.

1897   Adolphus Busch of St. Louis acquires the patent rights to the diesel engine.

1899   Frenchman Maxime Laubeuf creates the steam-driven *Narval*.

1900   Laubeuf creates the revolutionary diesel-powered *Aigrette*.

        John Holland sells his submarine, *Holland VI*, to the Navy for $160,000 on 11 April. The Navy commissions the vessel as USS *Holland* (SS–1) on 12 October, marking the start of the A class.

1903   The British have five Holland boats in commission for coastal defense service. The United States Navy commissions the seventh and last boat of the original Holland A class.

1906   Admiral Alfred von Tirpitz takes delivery on the Imperial German Navy's first (commissioned) submarine, the U–1.

1909   America imitates the diesel propulsion of *Aigrette* when the Electric Boat Company begins building the F class (SS–20 through 23) and the E class (SS–24 and 25) under a license from MAN at Fore River Shipyard in Quincy, Massachusetts. These engines were completed two years later by the New London Ship and Engine Company (Nelseco).

1911   The New London Ship and Engine Company is established as a subsidiary of the Electric Boat Company.

        The Busch Company comes to an agreement with Sulzer

Brothers, Ltd., of Switzerland, another diesel patent holder, to form the Busch-Sulzer Diesel Engine Company.

1913   Busch-Sulzer produces its first submarine diesel for the U.S. Navy.

Plagued by financial difficulty before the First World War, the Lake Torpedo Boat Company closes in November.

1915   Lake reorganizes and returns to business.

The Office of the Chief of Naval Operations is created.

Based on its experience developing *Schley* (T–1), the Navy Department authorizes two T-class fleet submarines on 2 March.

1916   Frederick Kollmorgen, an optical designer with Keuffel and Esser Optical Company, decides to capitalize on the demand for working, adjustable periscopes by forming his own company in conjunction with the Eastern Optical Company of New York City.

The Bureau of Construction and Repair and the Bureau of Steam Engineering produce the faster 15-knot, 800-ton, S-class submarines with the assistance of Electric Boat and Lake.

The revolutionary and hotly contested Appropriations Act of 29 August creates the Council of National Defense to take stock of domestic industrial capability to wage war and allows the Navy to begin building ships and submarines in much larger numbers. Congress specifically includes a provision in the bill designed to supplement earlier expenditures in this area and provide for the construction of thirty new submarines.

1917   The Act of 4 March reinforces the August legislation by adding eighteen more boats to the submarine construction program, and the Navy uses resources from the Naval Emergency Fund for twenty more.

The United States declares war against Germany on 6 April.

Secretary of the Navy Josephus Daniels approves the concept of a Submarine Standardization Board (Stirling board) on 20 June.

The War Industries Board is created in July to bring some order to resource allocation and price and wage control.

In October a second standardization board meets officially to consider the first board's recommendations and to establish the characteristics for future submarine construction. Chaired by retired Commander John S. Doddridge, this board includes some of the Navy's better submarine engineers and commanding officers, including Naval Constructor Commander Emory S. Land and Commander Chester W. Nimitz, representing Submarine Forces, Atlantic.

In testimony before the General Board in November, Commander Land discusses the soda-lime canister device developed by the American Can Company. The device draws the air across the exposed soda lime by means of a small intake fan, and works much better than the soda-lime Draeger device then in use on German U-boats. But two of these Gibbs units, while improving the air, would add an extra ton to the vessel's displacement.

1918   The American submarine force in Europe borrows four captured U-boats from the British and takes them to Portland, England, near Dorset, on 12 December for almost three weeks of tests and inspection.

It takes an executive order by President Woodrow Wilson on 4 March to force the nation's industry and military to heed the call for central direction in procurement and production.

1919   Electric Boat files claim with the Navy for compensation, citing extraordinary conditions and naval wartime priorities for its excessive expenditures on the T, O, R, and S classes. The company had endured the reduction in profit during the conflict pending the settlement of claims at the end of the war as promised by the technical bureaus and the Secretary of the Navy.

In the spring the Navy Department approves the temporary acquisition of six German submarines so that the technical bureaus and operational forces can take complete advantage of the advances made by their adversary during the war.

1919–21   Controversy rages between the Navy and Electric Boat over the quality of the submarine diesel engines provided by the latter's subsidiary, the New London Ship and Engine Company.

1920   In February the Navy Department orders an evaluation of Lake's potential as an effective submarine contractor.

By June the progress made at the New York Navy Yard on the diesel comes far enough to prompt Captain Thomas C. Hart to compare this new type of machinery favorably with the Nelseco design that afflicted the S class. Although the new system also experiences a torsional vibration problem, it does not display the severity that caused endless casualties in the S boats.

The Board on Submarine Claims meets in July.

1920–21   The Baxter and Taylor boards meet after the war to address the compensation claims filed with the Navy by private industry.

1922   The S–10 through 13 receive the new diesel system developed by the Bureau of Engineering at the New York Navy Yard as an alternative to Nelseco. This is the Navy's version of the successful MAN diesel that powered many German U-boats in the First World War.

1923   Submarine radios are deemed reliable on the surface up to 300 miles. In one test of surface capability, the R–22 communicates without any difficulty with a vessel near Block Island from a location off Cape Hatteras.

1924   The absence of product diversity at Lake and the Navy's determination to help Portsmouth mature into a first-class submarine yard causes the demise of the Lake Torpedo Boat Company. Simon Lake closes his small Bridgeport firm.

Diesel electric drive (DED) appears for the first time in the 2000-ton V–1. This type of electric surface propulsion does not require joining the diesel engines directly to the shafts, nor does it require the long, and frequently too elastic, propeller shafts necessary in diesel direct drive systems.

1926   The Submarine Officers Conference (SOC) is created.

1927–28   After SOC throws its support behind the U–135 concept in June and confirms Admiral Henry A. Wiley's initial feeling that a design accord is possible, the admiral continues to nurture these first signs of consensus. Upon leaving the General Board in November, Wiley enthusiastically endorses the revisionist submarine strategy, only now from his more influential position as Commander in Chief, U.S. Fleet.

Work at the Naval Research Laboratory and the General Electric Company produces an effective high-frequency radio transmitter for submarines. The model XE crystal-controlled, high-frequency transmitter allows the V–1 and V–2 to communicate on the surface over ranges between 200 and 500 miles, depending on position and atmospheric conditions.

1928   In February, Commander Thomas Withers, Commander Submarine Division 4, openly challenges the prudence of allowing a quest for greater surface speed to adversely affect the habitability and submerged performance of American submarines.

1929   Portsmouth and Electric Boat develop a system for pinning back the torpedo tube door shutters to provide the emerging torpedo with safe clearance.

American submarines employ periscopes with optical lengths of at least 27 feet. The Navy installs this type in the O and R classes still in use, as well as in the S–2. Thirty- and 34-foot models become standard in the rest of the S class and the V–1 through 6.

1930–31   The Bureau of Engineering, under Rear Admiral Harry E. Yarnell, proposes an arrangement with MAN by which the Navy would pay royalties on individual diesel engines built at New York Navy Yard from Augsburg's plans. Yarnell specifies the WV 28/38 (1500 horsepower) and the MV 40/46 (2000 horsepower) as the diesels for which the Navy would pay royalties according to the horsepower rating of the engine. Thus, should a new model or variation provide additional power, the Navy would have the option to build it, but at a price determined by the increased output. This proposition lays the foundation for an agreement with MAN signed on 25 February 1931.

1930   The London Treaty imposes a limit of 52,700 tons on the submarine force, and the Navy projects that 24,810 tons currently in service will become hopelessly antiquated by the end of 1936.

In September the Bureau of Construction and Repair proposes designs for *Cachalot* (V–8, SS–170) and *Cuttlefish* (V–9, SS–171) derived from the assets and perceived shortcomings of the U–135.

1930–32   The Navy equips twenty S boats with the Model TAR transmitter, which better utilizes the low power available on board submarines for radio communications. The TAR operates at both low and high frequency.

1931   Private-sector submarine construction resumes with the award of *Cuttlefish* to Electric Boat. It is the first new construction awarded to a private company since the Great War.

1932   The Bureau of Engineering, under Rear Admiral Samuel M. Robinson, initiates diesel engine competition for submarine propulsion.

Electric Boat acquires a special license to build two M(9)V 40/46 MAN diesels on 21 April.

1934   The Vinson-Trammel Act of 27 March authorizes naval construction up to the London Treaty limits of 1930.

Because congressional legislation demanded an equitable distribution of submarine contracts between naval and private shipyards, the Navy follows the *Porpoise* class of 1933 by assigning the newly authorized *Salmon* class to Portsmouth, Mare Island, and Electric Boat.

A design of approximately 1500 tons assumes the primary place within the submarine community as the best size and configuration to satisfy the Navy's desire for reliability, range, and habitability.

1935   In spite of the difficulty in finding space, the importance of submarine operations in the Pacific, Caribbean, and South Atlantic leads the Navy Department to install the first submarine air-conditioning system on board *Cuttlefish*.

1936   In March the General Board's final recommendations to the secretary for the 1937 construction program give 1450 tons as the "minimum compatible with a proper balance of the required military characteristics to meet the intended employment of the submarine."

1937   Assistant Secretary of the Navy Charles Edison receives the authority from Secretary of the Navy Claude Swanson to administer an accelerated construction program funded by New Deal recovery legislation and congressional appropriations.

1938   Edison receives complete authority over the increased shipbuilding program authorized by Secretary Swanson under the Vinson Act of 1938.

1940   Navy begins subsidizing the expansion of shipbuilding facilities; Manitowoc enters the submarine construction business as a follow-yard for Electric Boat.

The Seventy Percent Expansion Act is passed, marking the beginning of full-scale naval rearmament.

B. Submarine Characteristics and Construction Schedules

T Class

Characteristics
Displacement:	1107 tons normal
Design depth:	150 feet
Design speed:	surface=20 knots; submerged=10.5 knots
Engines:	1350 break horsepower (bhp) Nelseco diesels
Motors:	1350 bhp Electro Dynamic

Construction Schedule (according to keel laying date; built by Fore River under contract to Electric Boat)
T–1	21 June 1916
T–2	31 May 1917
T–3	21 May 1917

S Class

Characteristics (Electric Boat design)
Displacement:	854 tons normal
Design depth:	200 feet
Design speed:	surface=14.5 knots; submerged=11 knots
Engines:	1200 bhp Nelseco
Motors:	1500 bhp Electro Dynamic

Construction Schedule
S–1	12 November 1917
S–18 through 41	April 1918–April 1919
S–42 through 47	December 1920–February 1921

Characteristics (Lake Torpedo Boat Company design)
Displacement:	800 tons normal
Design depth:	200 feet
Design speed:	surface=15 knots; submerged=11 knots
Engines:	1800 bhp Busch-Sulzer
Motors:	1200 bhp Diehl

Construction Schedule
S–2	30 July 1917

Characteristics (Navy design)
Displacement:	875 tons normal (S–48 through 51=903 tons)
Design depth:	200 feet
Design speed:	surface=15 knots; submerged=11 knots
Engines:	1400 (2000 after S–4) bhp Nelseco, Bu-MAN, or Busch-Sulzer
Motors:	1200 bhp Westinghouse

Construction Schedule (built at Portsmouth Naval Shipyard and at Lake Torpedo Boat Company after the Navy rejected the S–2 design as inferior to the S–1 and S–3.)

S–4 through 17	December 1917–February 1920
S–48 through 51	December 1919–October 1920

V Class

Characteristics (V–1 through 3)

Displacement:	2000 tons normal
Design depth:	200 feet
Design speed:	surface=21 knots; submerged=8 knots
Engines:	4100 shaft horsepower Busch-Sulzer
Motors:	2400 shaft horsepower Elliot

Construction Schedule

V–1 and V–2	20 October 1921
V–3	16 November 1921

Characteristics (V–4 through 6)

Displacement:	2710–2730 tons normal
Design depth:	300 feet
Design speed:	surface=15–17 knots; submerged=8 knots
Engines:	3175 shaft horsepower Bu-MAN
Motors:	2400–2500 shaft horsepower Ridgeway or Westinghouse

Construction Schedule

V–4	1 May 1925
V–5	10 May 1927
V–6	2 August 1927

Characteristics (V–7 through 9)

Displacement:	1560 tons, 1110 tons, 1130 tons respectively
Design depth:	250 feet
Design speed:	surface=17 knots; submerged=8 knots
Engines:	3500 (Bu-MAN), 3100 (Bu-MAN), 3100 (EB-MAN) shaft horsepower respectively
Motors:	1750 (Electro Dynamic), 1600 (Electro Dynamic), 1600 (Westinghouse) shaft horsepower respectively

Construction Schedule

V–7	14 June 1930
V–8	21 October 1931
V–9	7 October 1931

Abbreviations

ASW	Antisubmarine warfare
Bd/I&S	Board of Inspection and Survey
BUC&R	Bureau of Construction and Repair
BUENG	Bureau of Engineering
BUORD	Bureau of Ordnance
BUSANDA	Bureau of Supplies and Accounts
BUSENG	Bureau of Steam Engineering
BUSHIPS	Bureau of Ships
CC	Construction Corps
CNO	Chief of Naval Operations
COMINCH	Commander in Chief, U.S. Fleet
COMSUBDIV	Commander Submarine Division
COMSUBFLOT	Commander Submarine Flotilla
COMSUBFOR	Commander Submarine Force
DDD	Diesel direct drive
DED	Diesel electric drive
DERD	Diesel electric reduction drive
EB	Electric Boat Company
EDO	Engineering Duty Officer
EES	Engineering Experiment Station
Elco	Electric Launch Company
FM	Fairbanks, Morse and Company
GENCORR	General Correspondence
GM	General Motors Corporation

HOR	Hooven, Owens, Rentschler Company
JAG	Judge Advocate General
MAN	Maschinenfabrik Augsburg-Nürnberg
Ms	Mobilization (German)
NA	National Archives, Washington, DC
Nelseco	New London Ship and Engine Company
NES	Naval Experimental Station
NIRA	National Industrial Recovery Act
OA	Operational Archives, Naval Historical Center, Washington, DC
RG	Record Group
R&D	Research and development
SECNAV	Secretary of the Navy
SFLM	Submarine Force Library and Museum, Groton, CT
SOC	Submarine Officers Conference
SSN	Nuclear-powered attack submarine
SUPSHIPS	Supervisor of Shipbuilding
UWD	Undersea Warfare Division
WNRC	Washington National Records Center, Suitland, MD

Notes

Introduction

1. Samuel P. Huntington, "The Defense Establishment: Vested Interests and the Public Interest" in *The Military Industrial Complex and U.S. Foreign Policy*, ed. Omer L. Carey (Pullman, WA, 1969), pp. 562–84.

2. For a recent analysis of the Royal Navy's response to technical innovation and its effect on strategy, see Jon Sumida, *In Defense of Naval Supremacy, Finance, Technology, and British Naval Policy, 1889–1914* (Boston, 1989).

3. William H. McNeill, *The Pursuit of Power* (Chicago, 1982), chap. 8.

4. The Bureau of Steam Engineering had its name changed in 1920 to the Bureau of Engineering. For the sake of simplicity, the acronym BUENG will be used in the text for both bureaus. Footnote citations will distinguish between the two names.

1. Points of Departure, 1880–1916

1. This section on the early development of submarines and submarine technology was derived from the following sources: Simon Lake, *The Submarine in War and Peace* (Philadelphia, 1918); Frank T. Cable, *The Birth and Development of the American Submarine* (New York, 1924); Naval History Division, Office of the Chief of Naval Operations, *Dictionary of American Naval Fighting Ships* (Washington, 1959–); R. K. Morris, *John P. Holland 1841–1914: Inventor of the Modern Submarine* (Annapolis, 1966); E. H. Jenkins, *A History of the French Navy* (London, 1973); E. Rössler, *Geschichte des deutschen Ubootbaus* (Munich, 1975); Norman Polmar, *The American Submarine* (Annapolis, 1981); Norman Friedman, *Submarine Design and Development* (Annapolis, 1984); T. Ropp, *The Development of a Modern Navy: French Naval Policy, 1871–1904* (Annapolis, 1987); Gary E. Weir, *Building the Kaiser's Navy: The Imperial Naval Office and German Industry in the Tirpitz Era, 1890–1919* (Annapolis, forthcoming 1991).

2. Elting E. Morison, *Men, Machines, and Modern Times* (Cambridge, MA, 1966), pp. 35–36.

3. The first *Plunger* was powered on the surface by a triple expansion steam engine built at the Columbian Iron Works of Baltimore. Submerged, the vessel depended upon battery-powered Electro-Dynamic electric motors. All displacement figures given in this book are surface displacement, not submerged.

4. The Otto-type gasoline engine was the forerunner of the standard four-stroke internal combustion engine. In the Otto cycle, the phases of suction, compression, combustion, expansion, and exhaust occur sequentially in a four- or two-stroke cycle reciprocating mechanism.

5. The fundamental strategic precepts of the French *Jeune Ecole* or Young School held that true command of the seas was impossible given the advent of the submarine, torpedo boat, and fast cruiser. This approach to naval conflict challenged the supremacy of the battleship and espoused a war against commerce that would endanger an adversary's ability to wage war. Volkmar Bueb, *Die "Junge Schule" der franzosischen Marine. Strategie und Politik 1875–1900* (Boppard a.Rh., 1971).

6. Nelseco operated as a subsidiary of Electric Boat until the former was closed in 1929. EB absorbed Nelseco and never really sold or disbanded the company.

7. H–1 through 3 patrolled the West Coast during the war, and the only boat in the M class, M–1, was not commissioned until 1918.

8. Carroll S. Alden, "American Submarine Operations in the War," *United States Naval Institute Proceedings* 46, no. 6 (Jun 1920) 811–50; no. 7 (Jul 1920): 1013–48

9. Vice Admiral Emory S. Land, interview by John T. Mason, Jr., 1963, pp. 67–68, Columbia University Oral History Project, Operational Archives, Naval Historical Center (hereafter OA).

10. Before 1931 EB subcontracted construction of submarines to Union Iron Works in San Francisco and Bethlehem (formerly Fore River) Shipbuilding Corporation in Quincy, Massachusetts, among others. After 1931 it built submarines at its own facility.

11. BUENG Memo, 1 Nov 1920, Series 1, file 1, box 2, Submarines/Undersea Warfare Division (hereafter Subs/UWD), OA.

12. A fleet submarine was defined as a vessel with sufficient size (1000 tons or more) and speed to keep up with and directly assist a surface fleet cruising at approximately 21 knots.

13. A first-class bid is an offer made by a prospective contractor to build a submarine according to the Navy's design specifications rather than its own.

14. Lake closed in November 1913, reorganized, and returned in 1915.

15. BUSENG and BUC&R, Memo for SECNAV, #27219–310, 30 Mar 1916, subj: Status of the work of Electric Boat Company, with regard to submarines, box 2158, General Correspondence of the Secretary of the Navy, 1916–1926 (hereafter SECNAV GENCORR 1919–26), RG 80, NA. For BUSENG's 1914 evaluation of the G-class boat built by Lake, see BUSENG to Aid for Material, 16 Jul 1914, box 408, General Correspondence of the Bureau of Steam Engineering, 1911–1922 (hereafter BUSENG GENCORR 1911–22), RG 19, Washington National Records Center, Suitland, MD (hereafter WNRC).

16. The designation "CC" stood for Construction Corps. This group, which existed between 1859 and 1940, was composed of a distinct group of highly skilled officers trained in ship design and construction at postgraduate schools in France and Great Britain. After 1901 some of this training took place at Massachusetts Institute of Technology.

A Corps of Naval Engineers was formally established by act of Congress in 1842. These officers received equality with the regular line in 1899; a separate category of specialists in sophisticated engineering matters was created in 1916. The latter held the designation Engineering Duty Officer (EDO). When BUC&R and BUENG combined to form BUSHIPS in June 1940, the EDOs were placed on a par with the regular line. The CC was formally abolished, absorbed into the line, and given the same status as the EDOs. The only professional distinction that then separated these two types of officers from the line was their expertise. For an excellent general discussion of the CC and the naval engineers, see Julius Augustus Furer, *Administration of the Navy Department in World War II* (Washington, 1959), pp. 234ff.

17. "Read by Naval Constructor Land at Meeting of the Executive Committee, August 11, 1915," file 1915, box 107, 420–15, General Board Subject Files 1900–1947, RG 80, NA.

18. Crescent Shipyard of Elizabethport, New Jersey, a private contractor, built many of the early Holland submarines, including *Holland* or SS–1. From 1900, when the Navy accepted SS–1, through to the commissioning of D–3 (SS–19) in 1910, every American submarine was powered on the surface by gasoline internal combustion engines. Gasoline and diesel power were not the only propulsion alternatives proposed in the first twenty years of the American submarine force. The Navy examined the possibilities of the T. V. Nordenfeldt steam propelled-design built in Sweden in 1885. A soda-boiler system was also considered as well as the early closed cycle proposal (1916–1922) made by Abner Neff. Congress appropriated $250,000 to install the Neff System in SS–108. Neff proposed using the diesels to run the submarine while submerged, drawing the oxidizer from tanks containing pressurized air. Exhaust would be expelled overboard after undergoing an atomization process that would make the gas bubbles so small they would easily mix with the seawater. Due to financial difficulties and personal illness, Neff never completed

the project and the SS–108 was never built. BUC&R to CNO, 16 Jun 1920; CNO to BUSENG and BUC&R, 19 Apr 1920; EB to CNO, 17 Jun 1918, box 1254, Correspondence Regarding Ships 1916–1925, RG 19, NA; "Neff Propulsion," 21 Apr 1922, General Board Hearings of 1922, vol. 2, pp. 397ff, Scholarly Resources Microfilm, OA.

19. Maschinenfabrik-Augsburg later became the premier German diesel manufacturer, Maschinenfabrik Augsburg-Nürnberg–MAN.

20. David T. Brown, *A History of the Sulzer Low-Speed Marine Diesel Engine* (Winterthur, Switzerland, 1984), pp. 5–7. This publication is in the author's possession courtesy of Sulzer Brothers, Ltd.

21. Fore River Shipbuilding Company, along with Union Iron Works of San Francisco, were EB's usual subcontractors for the actual construction of the boats it built for the Navy. Both companies later became part of the Bethlehem Shipbuilding Corporation.

22. General Dynamics, "History of the Electric Boat Company" (Unpublished MS, Groton, CT, 1949), p. II–24.

23. For an excellent discussion of both sides of the issue, see George T. Davis, *A Navy Second to None* (New York, 1940), pp. 224–32.

24. Bernard M. Baruch, *American Industry in the War: A Report of the War Industries Board* (Washington, 1921), p. 19; Memo for Captain Taylor, #27219–766, 26 Jul 1918, box 2163, SECNAV GENCORR 1916–26, RG 80, NA.

25. SECNAV Daniels to all Bureaus, #27219–337, 7 Dec 1916, box 2159, SECNAV GENCORR 1916–26, RG 80, NA. The Naval Emergency Fund Act authorized the Navy to requisition materials for defense construction, with compensation to be determined at a later date. Grosvenor B. Clarkson, *Industrial America in the World War: The Strategy Behind the Line, 1917–1918* (Boston, 1923), pp. 95–96.

26. SECNAV Daniels to all Bureaus, #27219–337, 7 Dec 1916, SECNAV GENCORR 1916–26, RG 80, NA.

27. Furer, *Administration of the Navy Department*, pp. 58ff. and 107ff.

28. BUC&R, BUSENG, and BUORD to SECNAV, #27219–337:1, 12 Apr 1917, box 2159, SECNAV GENCORR 1916–26, RG 80, NA. For more on the development of submarines in Britain during this period, see F. W. Lipscomb, *The British Su bmarine* (Greenwich, UK, 1975) and M.P. Cocker, *Observer's Directory of Royal Naval Su bmarines* (Annapolis, 1982).

29. "Notes on the Development of Submarines" by Lieutenant Commander Castle, Apr 1917, Series 1, file 3, box 2, Subs/UWD, OA.

30. Senior Member, General Board to SECNAV, 30 Nov 1917, box 107, 420–15, General Board Subject Files 1900–1947, RG 80, NA. For construction delay problems, see Inspector of Machinery, Quincy, MA to SECNAV (Operations), #28575–413, 27 Jan 1919; and CDR L. F. Welch, Prospective CO, AA–1 (T–1) to SECNAV, #28575–413, 20 Jan 1919, box 2556, SECNAV GENCORR 1916–26, RG 80, NA. To quote Commander Welch, "The Superintending Constructor at this plant has frequently declared to me that completion dates mean nothing." "This plant" refers to the Quincy plant of the Bethlehem Shipbuilding Corporation, one of EB's major subcontractors.

31. Emergency Fleet Corporation to Union Iron Works, #28747–33:1, 16 Aug 1917; Navy Department to Supervising Constructor—Union Iron Works, 2 Nov 1917; EB to SECNAV, 19 Dec 1917; SECNAV Daniels to Union Iron Works, 29 Dec 1917, box 2718, SECNAV GENCORR 1916–26, RG 80, NA. The Emergency Fleet Corporation was one of many agencies created to mobilize the various sectors of the American economy in the First World War. It controlled the construction of transport and merchant vessels and played a role as part of the Shipping Board as well as the War Council.

32. L class, 450 tons; T class, 1107 tons (prototype fleet submarines); O class, 491 tons; and R

class, 500–600 tons.

33. BUC&R to EB, 10 May 1917, vol. #184 (Grey Binders S–1/SS–105), Board of Inspection and Survey 1920–1942 (hereafter Bd I/S 1920–42), RG 38, NA.

34. EB to SECNAV with enclosure, 19 May 1917, vol. #184 (Grey Books S–1/SS–105), Bd I/S 1920–42, RG 38, NA.

35. Acting SECNAV Roosevelt to BUSENG, #28575–29, 21 Sep 1916, box 2554, SECNAV GENCORR 1916–26, RG 80, NA. The keel of the T–1 was laid in June 1916.

36. Often it seemed as if the Navy would buy its submarines wherever it could get them. In January 1918 the Navy quickly acquired the H–4 through H–9 from Electric Boat Company in a truly unusual agreement, but for the same imperative that caused Roosevelt to accelerate the T class. Imperial Russia purchased these boats just before the 1917 Bolshevik Revolution brought down the government of Tsar Nicholas II. Electric Boat had manufactured the H–4 through H–9 in knock-down condition on the West Coast and stored the prefabricated hull sections at Vancouver, British Columbia. They found it impossible to deliver the submarines to the Petrovski Wharf in St. Petersburg via Vladivostok because of the chaos accompanying the Russian Revolution.

37. This section is based on a reading of the Records of the Bureau of Construction and Repair and the Bureau of Steam Engineering held by the National Archives in Record Group 19. In addition the General Correspondence of the Secretary of the Navy (RG 80) and those of the Board of Inspection and Survey (RG 38) also provided vital insight into the problems of contract administration, design formulation, and construction supervision. In particular, the following documents were of great help:

File GO–1–S, 1917, box 200; Compensation Board to Solicitor, Purchase Order #50044, 4 Apr 1921, box 195, Compensation Board, RG 80, NA.

Charles Conard, BUSANDA to SECNAV, 28 Dec 1938; Inspector of Naval Material to Chief BUC&R, 19 Dec 1934; Inspector of Naval Material (Hartford, CT) to BUC&R and BUENG, 20 Dec 1934, box 3125, BUC&R GENCORR 1925–40, RG 19, NA.

"Steps in the Preliminary Design of a Submarine" (c. 1920), box 24; Commander Simmers to Lieutenant Commander Abbott, 27 Feb 1920, box 23; "Preliminary Stages: 1919 Fleet Submarines—History of Design" (V class)(c. 1920), box 23, Bureau of Construction and Repair Design Data for U.S. Naval Vessels 1914–1927, RG 19, NA.

"Navy Owned and Financed Industrial Facilities as of 31 August 1944," 31 Aug 1944, box 38; "Navy Contracts in War Procurement (Price Analysis Division of the Office of Procurement and Material), 13 Oct 1944, box 62, Records of the Secretary of the Navy James Forrestal 1940–1947, RG 80, NA.

38. The Navy often assisted in this phase of development because its facility at the David Taylor Model Basin provided excellent opportunities to study hydrodynamics, seakeeping qualities, and propulsion requirements in the towing tank. A great deal of this experience helped BUC&R and BUSENG improve their knowledge of submarine technology even before these bureaus collaborated on the design of the S-class boats.

39. The Compensation Board continued this function until 1942 when it was disestablished, and all of these responsibilities were centralized in BUSANDA. The Bureaus of Ordnance and Yards and Docks were the exceptions to this system. The former prepared the invitations to bid for some types of arms, projectiles, and gun forgings. It opened the bids, determined the awards, and prepared the contracts for the signature of the Secretary of the Navy. Yards and Docks did essentially the same for public works ashore, procuring the materials and labor required to build and maintain these facilities. The Office of the Judge Advocate General controlled leases and the purchase of land and buildings, as well as the bid-award process for the construction of naval vessels and some propulsion machinery. The Marine Corps was entirely independent of all Navy bureaus in its purchase and procurement functions.

40. The S-class design actually began as three separate but similar designs generated in 1916 by Electric Boat, Lake, and BUC&R. The two best designs from the Navy's viewpoint were the EB and BUC&R variations, so the Lake design was scrapped.

2. Questions of Strategy and Design

1. Naval War College Operations Problems, 1923 through 1927, boxes 14 and 15, Strategic Plans Division Records (hereafter Strategic Plans), OA. For an interesting discussion of the proper use of submarines, see CAPT George C. Day, "Submarines," Lecture delivered at the Naval War College, 16 Feb 1923, box 3, Lectures and Speeches Series 1, Strategic Plans. In this speech Captain Day said: "As to what submarines can do, or may be permitted to do, against enemy lines of communication and trade is a most difficult question. What they can do the Germans showed, but it is not in any way likely that we will ever use them in that way." (p. 5) Day was a graduate of the Naval War College with extensive experience in the Office of the Chief of Naval Operations (OPNAV). Barely seven months later he became Commander Submarine Divisions, Pacific Fleet. His inclination to avoid the German practice of permitting a war against commerce by individual submarines on patrol clearly indicates that this view was part of American naval policy after the Great War. Some American strategic thinkers at the Naval War College interpreted the German U-boat war against commerce as an act of desperation by the Imperial Navy. The U-boat was only modestly effective against warships, so merchantmen were the best alternative targets. From this standpoint submarines were best employed as scouts, screens for the surface fleet, or coastal defenders. There was a great deal of discussion about the operational, mechanical, and technological limits of the submarine, but virtually no appeal for a greater research and development effort to enable the submarine to play an expanded role. For example, see CAPT Lewis Coxe, USN, "Types and Missions of Surface Vessels, Submarines, and Aircraft," 4–5 Mar 1930, box 3, Lectures and Speeches Series 1, Strategic Plans, OA.

2. L. Y. Spear, Vice President of Electric Boat Company, published an article in 1916 entitled "The Submarine," in which he complained of the lack of consensus in the Navy on the role the submarine should play and the best type of submarine to fill that role. As far as he was concerned, "such apparent difference of opinion between prominent and capable officers can hardly fail to be confusing to both Congress and the public. It is therefore broadly speaking only accidental if out of all this confusion Congressional action results in appropriations for those sizes and types of submarines which would prove most efficient under actual war conditions." Spring 1916, EB Submarine Library Collection, Submarine Force Library and Museum, Groton, CT (hereafter SFLM).

3. Grant to Navy Department (Operations), #27219–337:1, 21 Mar 1917, box 2159, SECNAV GENCORR 1916–26, RG 80, NA.

4. Before 1910 independent or corporate inventors and patent holders had few options if the government used a patented product or process without proper payment. The procedure for obtaining redress was long, tortuous, and complicated. With the passage of the Act of June 25, 1910 (36 Stat., 851), the government received the right to use patents in times of emergency under the restraints and obligations defined in individual contracts. But the patent-holders who believed their rights were violated could bring suit in the Court of Claims for proper payment. This improved the government's reputation among inventors and the public while assuring the armed forces the necessary and best implements of war in times of conflict. *Annual Report of the Navy Department* (FY 1912 and 1913) (Washington, 1913 and 1914).

5. BUC&R, BUSENG, BUORD to SECNAV, #27219–337:1, 12 Apr 1917, box 2159, SECNAV GENCORR 1916–26, RG NA.

6. Stirling, Submarine Base Commander, New London to Commander Submarine Force, Atlantic Fleet, #27219–337:1, 28 Feb 1917; Stirling to the Naval Consulting Board, #27219–337:1, n.d. 1917, box 2159, SECNAV GENCORR 1916–26, RG 80, NA.

7. Stirling, Senior Member to Commander Submarine Force, #27219–501, 28 Jul 1917, subj: Standardization of Submarines, box 2161, SECNAV GENCORR 1916–26, RG 80, NA. Other characteristics: submerged radius of action = 8 hours at 8 knots (war battery); time to charge batteries = 6 hours; surface radius of action = 5500 miles at three-fourths power; deck armament = two 4-inch guns and one machine gun; radio communication range = at least 100 miles; air starting diesel engines; time from the surface to a 75-foot depth = 6 minutes.

8. Habitability is the term used to describe the quality of living conditions aboard a submarine, including space, air, bunks, and food.

9. One way to start a diesel engine is by compressed air, which turns the engine until sufficient compression temperature within the cylinder ignites the injected fuel. Once this first stroke is completed and the engine is running, the air source can be secured. For engines capable of reverse operation, the diesel is brought to a complete stop and then reversed using this same ignition technique. L. Wechsler, "Medium and High Speed Diesel Engines," in *Marine Engineering*, ed. Roy L. Harrington (New York, 1971), pp. 249–50.

10. Stirling, Senior Member to Commander Submarine Force, #27219–501, 28 Jul 1917, box 2161; Board on Standardization of Submarines (Doddridge board) to SECNAV, #28754–54, 3 Apr 1918 (date received), box 2163, SECNAV GENCORR 1916–26, RG 80, NA.

11. General Board to SECNAV, 22 Mar 1918, box 108, 420–15, General Board Subject Files 1900–1947, NA. The S-class design actually began as three separate but similar designs generated in 1916. The original intention was to assign the S–1 through 3 to different contractors. The S–1 was designed and built to Navy characteristics by Electric Boat. Lake did essentially the same thing with the S–2, and the design generated at BUC&R to meet the prescribed characteristics was built at Portsmouth Naval Shipyard. The two best designs from the Navy's viewpoint were the EB and BUC&R variations, so the Lake design was scrapped. The Navy trained the Lake people to build the bureau design and the department awarded fourteen S boats of this style to Lake (4) and Portsmouth (10). EB received a contract for twenty-four of its S boats, which according to its vice president, L. Y. Spear, "were essentially duplicates of the S–1 . . . including the engines." During the war, the original order for thirty-eight was increased considerably, but a few were cancelled when the conflict ended. In all, ten more contracts were awarded; EB built the S–42 through 47 and Lake took the S–48 through 51. Increasingly cognizant of the need for the U.S. submarine force to have longer-range boats for operations in European waters and the Pacific, these last ten boats were between 117 and 119 tons heavier with longer hulls and more powerful diesels. Electric Boat Memo "United States Submarines–S Class," Binder of S-Class General Information, Individual Submarine Historical Files, SFLM.

12. Final Trial Report of the S–1 (SS–105), 6 Dec 1920, box 1, Reports of the Material Inspection of Naval Vessels 1920–1942, Bd I/S 1920–1942, RG 38, NA. COMSUBDIV 12 to BUC&R via CNO, #27219–982:9, 14 May 1921, box 2164, SECNAV GENCORR 1916–26, RG 80, NA.

13. Robison to Commander U.S. Naval Forces Operating in European Waters, 15 Jan 1919, Series 1, file 1, box 1, Subs/UWD, OA.

14. In the German Imperial Navy the prefix UB stood for coastal defense submarines displacing approximately 100 to 500 tons depending upon the vessel's vintage. A UC prefix identified the smaller submarine minelayers (less than 600 tons). The large minelayers like the U–117 (displacement over 1100 tons) did not carry a UC designation. For further information see Rössler, *Geschichte des deutschen Ubootbaus*, p. 103.

15. Land to SECNAV via Chief BUC&R and CNO, #28766–177, 4 Feb 1919, box 2767, SECNAV GENCORR 1916–26, RG 80, NA.

16. Testimony on Fleet Submarine Design by Commander Emory Land, 6 Feb 1919, General Board Hearings of 1919, vol. 1, pp. 59ff., Scholarly Resources, OA.

17. Early in his career Vice Admiral Charles A. Lockwood had an opportunity to serve on board the UC–97 on its transatlantic crossing in 1919. He noted in his memoirs: "We had much to learn from these enemy boats. Their design was better than ours and they could dive much faster than we could." Lockwood, *Down to the Sea in Subs*, p. 103.

Early Ms-boats displaced roughly 700 to 800 tons, much like the American S class. Beginning with the U–43 built at the German Imperial Shipyard at Danzig, the Ms type went through many variations and functioned as the standard German submarine of the war. The Ms designation was an abbreviation for "mobilization." For further information see Rössler, *Geschichte des deutschen Ubootbaus*, chap. 2.

18. Memo, Assistant for Material to Director of Naval Intelligence, 27 May 1924, subj: German Submarines, Series 1, file 3, box 1, Subs/UWD, OA. Turning-circle tests were used to determine the radius of the tightest circle a submarine was capable of making. This important test provided data on maneuverability and the vessel's ability to take evasive action in case of attack.

19. Plans Committee to CNO, #28766–177:16 1/2, 12 May 1919, box 2767, SECNAV GENCORR 1916–26, RG 80, NA.

20. CNO (Submarine Section) to BUC&R, BUSENG, BUORD, #28766–177:197, 8 Nov 1919, box 2767, SECNAV GENCORR 1916–26, RG 80, NA. The freeboard is the vertical distance from the water line to the deck.

21. The design of the U–135 was one of the other submarines studied.

22. BUC&R to CNO via BUSENG, BUORD, #28766–177:227, 10 Apr 1920, box 2767, SECNAV GENCORR 1916–26, RG 80, NA.

23. Ibid., para. 3.

24. S–2 Preliminary Trial, 27 Aug 1919, box 1, Reports of Material Inspection of Naval Vessels 1920–42, Bd I/S, RG 38, NA.

25. BUC&R to CNO via BUSENG and BUORD, #28766–177:227, 10 Apr 1920, box 2767, SECNAV GENCORR 1916–26, RG 80, NA. For the vessel's state of repair, see #28766–177:123, box 2767, SECNAV GENCORR 1916–26, RG 80, NA. In July 1919 the U–140, an eagerly awaited example of the long-range U-cruisers, was acquired in poor state of repair, which kept it close to either the Portsmouth or the Philadelphia navy yards for its remaining useful life. It never eclipsed the U–111.

26. BUC&R to SECNAV, 15 Apr 1919, #28766–177:20; BUSENG to SECNAV, 18 Apr 1919, box 2767, RG 80, SECNAV GENCORR 1916–26, NA.

27. BUSENG to SECNAV, #28766–177:218, 16 Feb 1920; Memo for Captain Hart (list of desired apparatus), 19 Feb 1920; SECNAV to BUSENG, 5 Mar 1920, box 2767, SECNAV GENCORR 1916–26, RG 80, NA.

28. BUSENG Memo for Commander Fisher, #28766–239, 29 May 1919, box 2767, SECNAV GENCORR 1916–26, RG 80, NA.

29. Gibson to CAPT George Williams, #28766–177:249, 16 Aug 1920, box 2767, SECNAV GENCORR 1916–26, RG 80, NA. Gibson had extensive experience with the German boats, commanding the UC–97 and then the U–117.

30. Hart to SECNAV, #28766–177:236, 7 Oct 1920, box 2767, SECNAV GENCORR 1916–26, RG 80, NA.

31. Stirling to SECNAV, 28 Mar 1921, Series 1, file 3, box 1, Subs/UWD, OA; BUC&R to SECNAV, 18 May 1921, box 109, 420–15, General Board Subject Files 1900–47, RG 80, NA. For the perspective of a BUC&R naval constructor intimately involved with submarine design, see "Memo for the File," by Naval Constructor H. S. Howard, 14 Apr 1921, box 1254, Correspondence Regarding Ships 1916–1925, BUC&R, RG 19, NA.

32. Situation Relative to Submarines, 30 Jun 1921, General Board Hearings of 1921, vol. 2, pp. 304ff., Scholarly Resources Microfilm, OA. Captain Thomas Hart was an early supporter of Stirling's effort to push BUC&R into paying greater attention to the design and performance of

the German U-boats. Stirling to Hart, 13 Apr 1921; Hart to Stirling (with enclosed remarks on Stirling's letter of 28 Mar 1921), 22 Apr 1921; Stirling to Hart, 28 Apr 1921, folder 19, box 4, Papers of Admiral T. C. Hart, OA; James Leutze, *A Different Kind of Victory: A Biography of Admiral Thomas C. Hart* (Annapolis, 1981), pp. 67–73.

33. The Submarine Officers Conference, an advisory committee composed of experienced submariners, did not come into existence until 1926.

34. "The Situation Relative to Submarine," 30 Jun 1921, General Board Hearings of 1921, vol. 2, pp. 304ff., Scholarly Resources Microfilm, OA.

35. "Situation Relative to Submarines," 1 Jul 1921, General Board Hearings of 1921, vol. 2, pp. 356ff., Scholarly Resources Microfilm, OA.

36. General Board to SECNAV, 25 Jul 1921, box 109, 420–15, General Board Subject Files 1900–47, RG 80, NA. V–1 through V–3: Built at Portsmouth, 2000 tons, powered by Busch-Sulzer diesels, designed for 21 knots surface speed, 8 submerged.

37. Sims to President of the General Board, 3 Aug 1921, Series 1, file 3, box 1, Subs/UWD, OA.

38. "The Submarine Situation 1927," n.d., box 109, 420–15, General Board Subject Files 1900–47, RG 80, NA.

39. "Building Program, 1929—Submarines," 1 Apr 1927, General Board Hearings for 1927, vol. 1, pp. 67ff., Scholarly Resources Microfilm, OA.

40. Submarine Design and Building, 2 Jun 1927, Series 2, file 4, box 5, Subs/UWD, OA; William Manchester, *The Arms of Krupp* (Boston, 1968), pp. 352–54. At this session of the conference, the officers fully realized the difficulty of reproducing the U–135. Krupp had formed IvS. (Ingenieur-Kantoor voor Scheepsbouw), or Engineering Office for Shipbuilding, in The Hague to continue projects prohibited by the Versailles Treaty. As a representative of this Dutch company, Dr. Regenbogen, a diesel engineer and part of the wartime leadership at Krupp-Germania Shipyard, offered to sell different German submarine plans to the Navy. However, this firm would not have a complete set of plans because the German Imperial Naval Office awarded this larger Ms design to the Imperial Shipyard at Danzig. The plans disappeared after the war, presumably destroyed by the Allied Military Commission in control of the Danzig region.

41. Withers, COMSUBDIV 4 to SECNAV, 3 Feb 1928 and Wiley, CINCUS to SECNAV, 1 Apr 1928, box 109, 420–15, General Board Subject Files 1900–47, RG 80, NA. A new development, which must have encouraged Withers, was the improvement in radio communication for submarines in the 1920s.

42. Withers, "Design of Submarines," 14 Aug 1930, box 111, 420–15, General Board Subject Files 1900–47, RG 80, NA. Withers also resurrected the concept of a central authority governing submarine matters. He suggested a design control office that would both standardize American submarines and force industry to keep to the spirit, if not the letter, of the designs defined by the technical bureaus and the General Board. Withers to SECNAV, 14 Aug 1930, Series 1, file 6, box 4, Subs/UWD, OA.

43. Laning, President, Naval War College to SECNAV, 29 Aug 1930, box 111, 420–15, General Board Subject Files 1900–47, RG 80, NA.

44. Admiral Wiley became Commander in Chief, U.S. Fleet, on 8 November 1927 after serving as member and chairman of the General Board from 15 October 1925 to 8 November 1927.

45. The S- and V-class boats constantly confronted vibration and breakage problems with their diesel engines that significantly reduced their operational value.

46. "Building Program 1929—Submarines," 1 Apr 1927, General Board Hearings of 1927, vol. 1, pp. 67ff., Scholarly Resources Microfilm, OA. It should be recalled that the first three V-class submarines were the successors to the Navy's first generation of "fleet submarines," the 1107-ton T class. The V–1 through 3 (SS–163 through 165), or *Barracuda, Bass*, and *Bonita*, displaced 2000 tons and had a design speed of 21 knots, which was rarely reached even in the best of

conditions. The V–4 (SS–166), or *Argonaut*, is the exception in this class as the Navy's only attempt to imitate the German submarine minelayer of the First World War. She displaced 2710 tons. The V–5 and V–6 (SS–167 and SS–168), or *Nautilus* and *Narwhal*, were 2730-ton attempts to adapt this larger design to a conventional submarine configuration with 21-inch torpedoes.

47. "Characteristics of Cruiser and Mine-Laying Submarines," 17 Jul 1924, General Board Hearings of 1924, vol. 2, pp. 323ff., Scholarly Resources Microfilm, OA. See especially Admiral Jones's introduction on pages 323–24.

48. "General Characteristics and Design of Future Submarines," 6 Oct 1930, General Board Hearings of 1930, vol. 2, pp. 421ff., Scholarly Resources Microfilm, OA. The discussion of major characteristics begins on page 423.

49. "Military Characteristics for Submarines," 9 May 1928, General Board Hearings of 1928, vol. 1, pp. 129ff., Scholarly Resources Microfilm, OA. In particular see the comments of Rear Admiral W. H. Standley, director of the CNO's Office of Fleet Training, on the long-range inadequacy of the S-class, which begin on page 143 of the hearing record.

50. The Bu-MAN diesels were American copies of World War I-vintage German machinery designed and built for the U-boats by Maschinenfabrik Augsburg-Nürnberg. The Navy and Electric Boat each built diesel engines under license to MAN in the interwar period. The Navy produced its variation of the MAN diesels at the New York Navy Yard; these engines first appeared in the V–4, also called the SM–1, the Navy's only attempt at a large submarine minelayer.

51. "Submarines V–8 and V–9—Preliminary Design," 15 Sep 1930, box 110, 420–15, General Board Subject Files 1900–47, RG 80, NA. Day, Senior Member of the General Board to SECNAV, 11 Aug 1930, box 111, 420–15, General Board Subject Files 1900–47, RG 80, NA.

52. The intermediate designation here falls roughly between the old 800-ton S-class and the much larger 2000-ton, V-class fleet submarines.

53. The Navy developed these engines from the MAN machinery that powered Germany's U-boats in the First World War. The origins of the Bu-MAN diesels are explored in the chapter on propulsion.

54. The exact standard displacements of the V–8 and V–9 are 1111 tons and 1130 tons respectively.

55. Picking to Chairman of the General Board, 10 Feb 1934; Styer to Chairman of the General Board, 8 Feb 1934, box 111, 420–15, General Board Subject Files 1900–47, RG 80, NA.

56. *Salmon*: 1449 tons, 5 officers, 50 enlisted, designed for 21 knots surfaced, 9 submerged. *Sargo*: 1450 tons, 5 officers, 50 enlisted, designed for 20 knots surfaced, 8.75 submerged. Both keels were laid in 1934. A discussion of the Hooven-Owens-Rentschler diesels, which powered the SS–182 through 184, the SS–188 through 190, and the SS–194 in these two classes, appears in the chapter on propulsion.

57. SOC to CNO, 28 Jun 1937, box 112, 420–15, General Board Subject Files 1900–47, RG 80, NA. For Admiral Hart's position on the smaller submarines, see Chairman of the General Board to SECNAV, 24 Mar 1937, box 112, 420–15, General Board Subject Files 1900–47, RG 80, NA.

58. Chairman of the General Board to SECNAV, 13 Mar 1936, box 112, 420–15, General Board Subject Files 1900–47, RG 80, NA.

59. "Characteristics of Submarines," 24 May 1938, box 112, 420–15, General Board Subject Files 1900–47, RG 80, NA. This hearing clearly reveals BUENG's desire to stay with the 1450-ton boats in order to perfect and standardize the type. See the testimony of Commander R. W. Paine and Lieutenant Commander E. H. Bryant of the BUENG for this viewpoint. For the consistency of the SOC's preference in spite a lingering attachment to the 800-ton type, see SOC Memo, 21 Apr 1938, Series 1, file 8, box 4, Subs/UWD, OA.

60. By 1935 the new role for the submarine as defined by Withers and the Naval War College became part of the deployment suggested by the Commander in Chief, U.S. Fleet, for the Blue

submarine forces in an Orange war in the Pacific. Study of Initial Employment—Blue Submarines, Dec 1935, Series 3, box 73, Strategic Plans, OA.

61. Seventy Percent Expansion Act and Submarine Construction Schedules (SOC Memo), 9 Sep 1940; Shipyard Construction Assignments (SOC Memo), 9 Jul 1940, Series 1, file 5, box 2, Subs/UWD, OA.

3. A Firm Foundation?

1. In this context "mission" describes the fundamental reason for the Navy's existence and the task to which every naval activity is dedicated, namely, the defense of the United States. National defense was equally important to the private sector, but private firms carried the additional burden of guaranteeing the financial health and technical growth of their companies. These goals were not always in harmony with the Navy's priorities.

2. SECNAV Daniels to Rep. L. Padgett, #28575–19:5, 3 Mar 1916, Memo for SECNAV from BUC&R and BUSENG, #28575–19, 13 Mar 1916, box 2554, SECNAV GENCORR 1916–26, RG 80, NA.

The Navy decided to award the S–1 to EB, the S–2 to Lake, and the S–3 to Portsmouth. The EB design met naval requirements, but the Lake variation did not. This led the Navy to allow EB to build its own design; BUC&R assembled its version at Portsmouth and required Lake to do the same in both Bridgeport and at its subcontractors yards. Lake occasionally employed Newport News Shipyard and the California Shipbuilding Company, among others, to build some submarines. This was the case with the O–14 through 16. Until 1931 all of Electric Boat's submarines were built by subcontractors like the Fore River Shipbuilding Co. of Quincy, MA, and Union Iron Works of San Francisco (both of which were later absorbed by the Bethlehem Shipbuilding Corporation), Moran Shipbuilding Company, and the Seattle Shipbuilding and Drydock Company.

3. Wright to LCDR W. J. Butler, Bd I/S, 14 Aug 1919, vol #185 (Grey Binders S–3/ SS–107), Bd I/S, RG 38, NA.

4. Wright to LCDR J. Van de Carr, 19 Jan 1920, Series 1, file 1, box 2, Subs/UWD, OA.

5. The compensation issue is discussed in greater detail below.

6. Williams, Memo for the CNO, #28729:159–3, 14 Apr 1921, box 2708, SECNAV GENCORR 1916–26, RG 80, NA; Memo for the CNO, #29197–10, 17 Feb 1921, box 3145, SECNAV GENCORR 1916–26, RG 80, NA.

7. Lake Torpedo Boat Company to the General Board, 18 Jun 1918, subj: Naval Appropriations Bill, box 108, 420–15, General Board Subject Files 1900–47, RG 80, NA. The last of the G-class submarines built by Lake, the G–3, was used as an experimental diesel vessel. Because their gasoline engines did not provide adequate or reliable power, the G–3 and its sister ships were scheduled for retirement when the G–3 was drafted as a test platform for a Busch-Sulzer diesel imported from the Sulzer Company of Winterthur, Switzerland, via New York by the Navy and Lake. Agreement between the Navy and Busch-Sulzer for a diesel installation in the G–3, 21 Oct 1912, box 826, BUSENG GENCORR 1911–22, RG 19, WNRC.

8. These nine were the S–2, S–14 through 17, and S–48 through 51.

9. "Report of the Board based on full and careful investigation of the organization and methods of the Lake Torpedo Boat Company...," #28721–405:1, 17 Mar 1920, SECNAV GENCORR 1916–26, RG 80, NA.

10. Sen. Frank Brandegee to SECNAV, #28575–230, 14 Apr 1920, box 2555, SECNAV GENCORR 1916–26, RG 80, NA.

11. Williams, Memo for the CNO, #27219–998, 5 May 1921, box 2165, SECNAV GENCORR 1916–26, RG 80, NA.

12. Williams, Memo for the CNO regarding Simon Lake's letter of 9 May 1921 and Memo for the CNO regarding the speech of the Hon. George B. McClean, #27219–998, 12 May 1921, box 2165, SECNAV GENCORR 1916–26, RG 80, NA.

13. Clarkson, *Industrial America*, pp. 48–49. For a brief treatment of the evolution of the WIB from the Naval Consulting Board through the National Defense Advisory Commission, see P. A. Koistinen, *The Military-Industrial Complex, A Historical Perspective*, pp 20–41.

14. Contract for the SS–60/61 (T–2/3), #28575–11:2, 8 Jan 1916, box 2554, SECNAV GENCORR 1916–26, RG 80, NA.

15. In 1919, Lake tried to retain the services of one of the expert engineers with the Pneumercator Company at the going rate of $13.50 per day. The Compensation Board refused, offering only $10 per day because that was the rate fixed in the contract. Cost Inspector (BUSANDA) to Compensation Board, 17 Apr 1919; Cost Inspection Board (Compensation Board) to Lake Torpedo Boat Company, 26 Apr 1919, file G–9022, box 200, Compensation Board, RG 80, NA.

16. EB, Memo on Fixed Price Submarines and Submarine Parts for SECNAV, #28816–32:92, 16 Oct 1920, box 2835, SECNAV GENCORR 1916–26, RG 80, NA. This document is an excellent synopsis from EB's point of view of the difficulties plaguing the company during mobilization. For an example of the delay of claims until the end of the war as standard Navy procedure, see Navy Department to BUC&R, #28721–212, 1 Mar 1919, box 2695, SECNAV GENCORR 1916–26, RG 80, NA.

17. California Shipbuilding Co. to SECNAV Daniels, #28585–121, 15 Apr 1918, SECNAV GENCORR 1916–26, NA.

18. In 1921 the Navy addressed this problem when SECNAV Daniels issued an order allowing the Navy to expect the contractor to include all changes authorized by the Navy Department before delivery. However, no design or detail changes could be incorporated after delivery or during the 6-month and 10-day trial period. CNO to BUENG, BUC&R, BUORD, Bureau of Navigation, #27219–971, 4 Jan 1921, box 2164, SECNAV GENCORR 1916–26, RG 80, NA.

19. EB to BUC&R, 20 Sep 1918, box 3, BUSHIPS Board on Submarine Claims 1918–22, RG 19, NA.

20. For an interesting illustration of the Navy's suspicions and hard-line reaction, especially in the case of the T-class submarines, see Navy Dept. to EB, 7 Dec 1920; Superintending Constructor, Quincy, MA to BUC&R, 26 Mar 1917; BUC&R to Navy Dept. Solicitor, n.d. 1917; BUSENG to Navy Dept. Solicitor via BUC&R, 26 Mar 1917, box 1256, Correspondence Regarding Ships 1916–25, RG 19, NA.

21. CAPT Henry Williams (CC), Superintending Constructor, Quincy, MA to the Board on Submarine Claims, #28575–414:2, 21 Jul 1920, box 2556, SECNAV GENCORR 1916–26, RG 80, NA.

22. BUC&R and BUENG to SECNAV, 20 Mar 1923, box 1256, Correspondence Regarding Ships 1916–25, RG 19, NA. According to item 20 in this document, "Attention is invited to the Superintending Constructor's statement that the delay of this vessel [T–2] was not caused by preference given to destroyer construction but to preference given to bonus-bearing submarines."

23. The boats for which EB claimed compensation were the AA (T)–1 through 3, O–3 through 10, R–1 through 4, and S–1 built at Fore River Shipbuilding, and the R–15 through 20 and S–30 through 41 built by Union Iron Works.

24. Nelseco was responsible for the diesels that powered EB submarines. EB's Electric Launch Company built pleasure boats for private customers and small craft for the Navy at its plant in Bayonne, NJ. Electro-Dynamic manufactured electric motors for EB submarines. National Torpedo provided the obvious service, Vanadium supplied Nelseco with castings for its diesel motors, and General Ordinance built air compressors.

25. The Macy board was also known as the Shipbuilding Labor Adjustment Board, the central

control agency for the regulation of wartime shipbuilding labor rates.

26. For all information on the activities of the Baxter board, see Records of the Submarine Compensation Board, 1918–1922, boxes 1 and 3, Submarine Claims 1918–22, RG 19, NA.

27. Taylor to SECNAV, 21 Jun 1922; Taylor to SECNAV, 13 Sep 1922, box 3, Submarine Claims 1918–22, RG 19, NA.

28. SECNAV to Harold L. Ickes, Federal Administrator of Public Works, Federal Emergency Administration, 22 Jan 1934, box 18 (Portsmouth Folder), Assistant SECNAV Alpha Files, RG 80, NA. The NIRA money passed Congress on 15 June 1933 and received Franklin Roosevelt's signature the next day. The President's order released $238 million for the Navy.

29. Davis, *A Navy Second to None*, pp. 358–62.

30. Metacentric height, a major indicator of hull stability afloat, is the intersection of a vertical line through the center of buoyancy, slightly displaced from its equilibrium, with a line connecting the center of gravity and the vessel's normal center of buoyancy. The vessel is stable if the metacenter (intersection) lies above the center of gravity. The distance between the metacenter and the center of gravity is the metacentric height.

31. President, Bd I/S to Senior Member, Sub-Bd I/S, 22 Mar 1932, box 6 (S–10; SS–115), Reports of Material Inspection of Naval Vessels 1920–42, Bd I/S, RG 38, NA; SECNAV Swanson to EB, #SS176/L4–3(341025), 23 Nov 1934; BUC&R and BUENG to SECNAV, #SS176 to 181/S43, 13 Mar 1936, box 4101, SECNAV GENCORR 1926–40, RG 80, NA.

32. Rep. Carl Vinson (D-Georgia) was instrumental in working with Roosevelt to insert a naval provision in the 1934 NIRA legislation that created 20,000 new jobs in the shipbuilding industry after the passage of the act.

33. Spear to Inspector of Machinery and Superintending Constructor, Groton, #SS171/L4–3 (340208), 3 Jan 1934, box 4090, SECNAV GENCORR 1926–40, RG 80, NA.

34. BUC&R and BUENG to JAG, #SS171/L4–3 (360527), 27 May 1936, box 4090, SECNAV GENCORR 1926–40, RG 80, NA.

Some legislation passed in Roosevelt's first term initially endangered the supply of vital raw materials to the Navy's contractors. The Walsh-Healy Act, which limited the weekly hours of the average worker to between 40 and 48 on government contracts resulted in a sharp drop in the number of contractors willing to bid on Navy steel contracts. In February 1937 the Navy received no bids at all for 25 million pounds of steel for all types of ships. The Navy awarded only 7 million pounds of steel contracts to bidders competing for navy yard construction of destroyers and submarines. "Madame Perkins and the Submarines," *Chicago Tribune*, 20 Feb 1937; "Government Steel," *Journal*, (Providence, RI), 21 Feb 1937, box 8, Assistant SECNAV Alpha File, RG 80, NA.

The extent of EB's national and international business was examined by the Senate's Nye Committee (Special Committee on Investigation of the Munitions Industry) in 1936. The committee found the extent of EB's submarine patents and the consequent involvement of the company in the international submarine industry particularly disturbing in spite of assertions by Emory Land and others that some of EB's patents had already expired. "Munitions Industry," *Report of the Special Committee on Investigation of the Munitions Industry,* 74th Cong., 1st sess., 1936, S. Res. 206.

35. Testimony by Rear Admiral G. J. Rowcliff, USN, JAG, before the House Committee on Naval Affairs, n.d. 1938, box 7, Assistant SECNAV Alpha File, RG 80, NA. The Tobey (Charles W. Tobey, R–New Hampshire) Amendment to the Vinson-Trammel Act of 1934 set an arbitrary limit of 10 percent on profit-taking from naval contracts. This portion of the bill was not the work of the measure's major architect, Representative Vinson. The amendment was a political maneuver to satisfy those among the American people who demanded control over the "merchants of death." Michael A. West, "Laying the Legislative Foundation: The House Naval Affairs Committee and

the Construction of the Treaty Navy, 1926–1934" (Ph.D. Diss., Ohio State University, 1980), pp. 403ff.

36. Spear to Hart, 22 Jul 1938, box 112, 420–15, General Board Subject Files 1900–47, RG 80, NA.

37. Spear to Hart, 24 Mar 1939, box 112, 420–15, General Board Subject Files 1900–47, RG 80, NA.

38. Hart to Spear, 25 Mar 1939, box 112, 420–15, General Board Subject Files 1900–47, RG 80, NA.

39. Rowcliff, Memo for the Assistant SECNAV, n.d. (probably Mar) 1937; Assistant SECNAV to all Bureaus, 15 Mar 1937, box 7, Assistant SECNAV Alpha File, RG 80, NA.

40. Assistant SECNAV Edison, Memo on the Construction Program, 9 May 1938, box 7, Assistant SECNAV Alpha File, RG 80, NA.

41. DeFrees to Edison, 6 Dec 1938, box 7, Assistant SECNAV Alpha File, RG 80, NA.

42. A. T. Church, Memo on New Construction, 4 Apr 1939, box 7, Assistant SECNAV Alpha File, RG 80, NA; Davis, *A Navy Second to None*, p 380. For more on the Vinson acts, see Michael A. West, "Laying the Legislative Foundation."

43. EB to SUPSHIPS, Groton, 14 Aug 1940 and 24 Jul 1940; Acting SECNAV Lewis Compton to EB, 23 Sep 1940, box 1986, BUSHIPS GENCORR 1940–45, RG 19, WNRC. Later commitments to this program brought the total Navy investment up to over $4 million for the expansion of the yard under Navy contract NOb–1541. After the beginning of the Second World War a further expansion was authorized under contract NOb–380, which cost over $9 million. Liaison Officer for the Price Adjustment Board, CAPT N. L. Rawlings, USN, Head of Shipbuilding Division, BUSHIPS to Price Adjustment Board, 12 Jun 1942, box 405, BUSHIPS General Correspondence 1940–45, RG 19, WNRC.

44. EB-Manitowoc Licensing Agreement, 14 Sep 1940; Manitowoc to SUPSHIPS, Manitowoc, 2 and 22 Nov 1940, box 1986, BUSHIPS GENCORR 1940–45, RG 19, WNRC.

45. For a discussion of these motives, see BUSHIPS to Bureau of Supplies and Accounts, 23 May 1941, box 1987, BUSHIPS GENCORR, RG 19, WNRC.

46. Sun Shipbuilding and Drydock Co. of Chester, Pennsylvania, also tried to enter the market in 1933 but was outbid by Electric Boat. According to communications between Sun, Navy JAG, and BUC&R and BUENG, the company had to raise its price beyond the range acceptable to the Navy in order to cover the cost of royalties on EB submarine patents. The bureaus were not in the position at the time to grant Sun a waiver of patent liability, given the importance of EB to the Navy's new plans for construction in the early 1930s. Sun Shipbuilding to JAG, #SS/L4–2 (350703–1)18, Jul 1935; BUC&R and BUENG to JAG, #SS/L4–2 (350703–1), 30 Jul 1935, box 4020, SECNAV GENCORR 1926–40, RG 80, NA.

47. SUPSHIPS, Manitowoc to BUSHIPS, 10 Apr 1941; EB Purchasing Agent, F. B. Bently to EB-Manitowoc Representative, Eric H. Ewertz, 25 Feb 1941; EB to SUPSHIPS, Groton, 9 Feb 1942, box 1987, BUSHIPS GENCORR 1940–45, RG 19, WNRC.

EB was set up as a conduit for all of the unique materials and systems needed to build the *Gato*-class boats after EB designs. If these items could be procured locally and were not a specific design requirement, then Manitowoc, Mare Island, and Portsmouth were free to purchase them locally. If the items were specific to the design as set down by EB, then the company was used as a conduit and obliged to order these materials and systems for all of the yards building the *Gato* class, billing the Navy at cost, absorbing all manpower and administrative costs. This is another reason for EB's dissatisfaction with the arrangement; the administrative costs were staggering.

4. On-the-Job Training

1. General Manager's Report on Postwar Transition, 18 Nov 1918, box 22, Elmer Sperry Papers (Accession #1893), Hagley Museum Archive.

2. Ibid. Italics in the original.

3. Because of its pivotal importance, the diesel engine problem is explored in chapter 5.

4. The G–3 (SS–31) had six 18-inch torpedo tubes, but two were mounted on the deck outside the hull.

5. Developments in Submarine Design, Testimony of Lieutenant Commander Bogusch, 27 Dec 1918, General Board Hearings of 1918, vol. 4, pp. 1389ff., Scholarly Resources Microfilm, OA. For the technical details on the torpedoes discussed in this section, see E. W. Jolie, *A Brief History of U.S. Navy Torpedo Development* (Newport, RI, 1978).

6. BUORD to CNO via BUC&R, 6 Dec 1918; BUC&R to CNO, 18 Dec 1918, box 1301, Correspondence Regarding Ships, RG 19, NA. The structural changes involved torpedo-tube placement and torpedo storage, not tube size.

　　Although of the same class, the S boats produced by EB and Portsmouth had their differences reflecting the preferences in construction technique and engineering peculiar to each yard. These slight variations persisted throughout the history of American submarine construction and are recognizable in the fleet submarines of the Second World War, as well as in the way each yard modified some of these submarines for greater submerged speed (GUPPY Program) after the war.

7. Torpedo Tube Shutters, 16 Sep 1920, vol. 188, Bd I/S (Gray Binders), RG 38, NA; BUC&R to Superintending Constructor, Quincy, 16 Sep 1920, box 62, Reports of the Material Inspection of Naval Vessels 1920–42, RG 38, NA.

8. COMSUBDIV Asiatic to CNO via COMSUBDIV Pacific, 23 Dec 1924, box 3, Reports on the Material Inspection of Naval Vessels, Bd I/S, RG 38, NA.

9. For a general discussion of the deck-gun issue as a reflection of the offensive-defensive debate over the submarine's strategic role, see RADM Thomas Hart, General Board Memo, 17 Jan 1938, box 112, 420–15, General Board Subject Files 1900–47, RG 80, NA.

10. Day, "Submarines," 16 Feb 1923, box 3, Lectures and Speeches Series 1, Strategic Plans, OA; Louis A. Gebhard, *Evolution of Radio-Electronics and Contributions of the Naval Research Laboratory* (Washington, 1979), pp. 55–57.

11. BUSHIPS to CNO, 25 Oct 1940, subj: Underwater Reception of Radio Signals, box 4, Confidential Correspondence Regarding Research and Design of Radio and Other Communications Apparatus, BUENG, RG 19, NA.

12. ASW Listening Devices, Testimony of Major R. A. Millikan, 18 Jan 1918, General Board Hearings of 1918, vol. 1, pp. 83ff., Scholarly Resources Microfilm, OA; Willem Hackmann, *Seek and Strike, Sonar, Anti-Submarine Warfare and the Royal Navy, 1914–54* (London, 1984), pp. 39–43, 89–95.

13. Marvin Lasky, "A Historical Review of Underwater Acoustic Technology, 1916–1939, with Emphasis on Undersea Warfare," *U.S. Navy Journal of Underwater Acoustics*, 24 (Oct 1974): 616–18.

14. For information on Frederick Kollmorgen, see Kollmorgen Corporation, *The Submarine Periscope, 1916–1966* (Northhampton, MA, 1966), pp. 4–9; Bruce H. Walker, *Periscopes, People, and Progress* (North Adams, MA, 1984), pp. 1–5.

15. EB to BUC&R, 14 Feb 1918, box 2129, Correspondence Regarding Ships 1916–25, BUC&R, RG 19, NA.

16. EB to BUC&R, 14 Feb 1918; BUC&R to Navy Compensation Board (attached memo), 6 Mar 1918; Chief Constructor to EB, n.d. (Mar 1918), box 2129, Correspondence Regarding Ships

1916–25, BUC&R, RG 19, NA; Electric Boat Purchase Order #50145 (Supplement), 16 Apr 1918, box 196, Navy Compensation Board, RG 80, NA.

17. Memo for Assistant Secretary's Office—Mr. Howe, 22 May 1918, box 2129, Correspondence Regarding Ships 1916–25, BUC&R, RG 19, NA.

18. BUC&R to Cost Inspectors at Quincy, MA and Groton, CT, 17 May 1918; Cost Inspector of the U.S. Navy to Compensation Board, 27 May 1918; Navy Department to BUC&R, 24 Jul 1920, box 196, EB Purchase Order #50145, Compensation Board, RG 80, NA.

19. CDR F. X. Gygax to OPNAV (Material Office), #27219–849, 15 Jan 1919; T. S. Boyd to Gygax, #27219–849, 27 Jan 1919, box 2163, SECNAV GENCORR 1916–26, RG 80, NA.

20. Preliminary Trials of the S–3, 15 Jun 1920, box 2, Reports of the Material Inspection of Naval Vessels 1920–42, Bd I/S, RG 38, NA.

21. Memo for RADM D. W. Taylor, BUC&R, 15 Jan 1929, box 2, Periscope File, Submarine Board 1928–29, RG 80, NA.

22. Preliminary Trial of the S–50, 15–16 Mar 1922, box 23, Reports of the Material Inspection of Naval Vessels 1920–42, Bd I/S, RG 38, NA; Preliminary Trial of the S–48, 5–9 Sep 1922, box 22, Reports of Material Inspection of Naval Vessels 1920–42, Bd I/S, RG 38, NA.

23. Official Trials of the V–1, 7 Jul–6 Aug 1926, box 24, Reports of the Material Inspection of Naval Vessels 1920–42, Bd I/S, RG 38, NA.

24. Final Trial of the V–9, 30 Oct–2 Nov 1934, box 58, Reports of the Material Inspection of Naval Vessels 1920–42, Bd I/S, RG 38, NA.

25. Captain King, later admiral, served as Chief of Naval Operations and Commander in Chief, U.S. Fleet, combined functions as COMINCH, during the Second World War.

26. COMSUBDIV 3 to BUC&R, #28747–406, 15 Jun 1923, box 2720, SECNAV GENCORR 1916–26, RG 80, NA.

27. Ibid.

28. Ventilation and Air Purification, 20 Nov 1917, General Board Hearings of 1917, vol. 2, pp. 617ff; Air Purification, 22 Nov 1917, General Board Hearings of 1917, vol. 2, pp. 645ff.; Air Purification, 21 Dec 1917, General Board Hearings of 1917, vol. 2, pp. 633ff., Scholarly Resources Microfilm, OA; Notes on Carbon Dioxide Elimination..., #SS/S38–1 (291018), 18 Oct 1929, box 4024, SECNAV GENCORR 1926–40, RG 80, NA.
 The Bureau of Medicine and Surgery suggested that oxygen flasks would increase crew comfort. But only very compact flasks would have made this possible. In addition Sperry had a promising hydrogen detector in development. But, until it became available, the Navy and the Bureau of Standards provided the submariners with a primitive substitute. CNO to Bureau of Medicine and Surgery, #27219–803, 22 Nov 1918, box 2163, SECNAV GENCORR 1916–26, RG 80, NA; "Air Purification in Submarines," 22 Nov 1917, vol. 2, pp. 645ff., General Board Hearings of 1917, Scholarly Resources Microfilm, OA.

29. LCDR Thomas F. O'Brien, S-Class Ventilation Memo, #28816–356:1, 25 Feb 1923, box 2836, SECNAV GENCORR 1916–26, RG 80, NA. The fairwater was the portion of the vessel that cleared the water when surfaced.

30. CNO to BUC&R, 30 Jul 1923, Series 1, file 1, box 2, Subs/UWD, OA.

31. CO USS S–3 to Bd I/S, 27 Jan 1927, Material Inspection of the S–3, 3 Feb 1927, box 2, Reports of the Material Inspection of Naval Vessels, Bd I/S, RG 38, NA; Bureau of Medicine and Surgery to CNO, #SS/S–38–1(270920), 20 Sep 1927; BUC&R to CNO and Bureau of Medicine and Surgery, #SS/S–38–(15) (DS), 3 Dec 1927, box 4024, SECNAV GENCORR 1926–40, RG 80, NA.

32. John D. Alden, *The Fleet Submarine in the U.S. Navy, A Design and Construction History* (Annapolis, 1979), p. 48; CNO Report on Air Conditioning, 3 Oct 1935, series 1, file 8, box 4,

Subs/UWD, OA; COMSUBFOR U.S. Fleet to CNO, #SS/S38–1 (340710–1) 16 Sep 1935, SECNAV GENCORR 1926–40, RG 80, NA.

5.   The Achilles' Heel

1. F class: 330 tons, diesels manufactured by Nelseco and Craig Shipbuilding, Long Beach, California.

2. Final Trials of the H–1, 1913, vol. 67 (Gray Binders), Bd I/S, RG 37, NA; Preliminary Trials of the H–2, 13 Aug to 17 Sep 1913, vol. 68 (Gray Binders), Bd I/S, RG 38, NA.

3. Final Trials of the H–2, 20 May 1914, vol. 68 (Gray Binders), Bd I/S, RG 38, NA.

4. Investigation into the Cracked Housing of the Port Engine on board USS K–1, #26283–1127:1, 14 Sep 1916, box 1755, SECNAV GENCORR 1916–26, RG 80, NA. The governor is the system employed to keep the diesels running at the desired speed.

5. The term machinery is used in this chapter to denote a vessel's propulsion system.

6. Ibid., p. 2. For the report on weak castings in the K–6, see Submarine Housings—Main Engines, 3 Aug 1917, box 64, Reports of the Material Inspection of Naval Vessels 1920–42, Bd I/S, RG 38, NA. A two-stroke diesel engine employs a scavenging apparatus to inject air to facilitate the compression stroke and also to remove the exhaust after the power stroke, thus eliminating the need for two of the four strokes involved in standard operation. Intake-compression-power-exhaust is replaced by compression-power, with the scavenger performing the function of the first and last strokes.

7. Griffin to Thomas Robins, Secretary of the Naval Consulting Board, #188493–639–D, 23 May 1916, box 62, Naval Consulting Board Correspondence Files 1915–23, RG 80, NA.

8. Testimony of Naval Constructor H. S. Howard, 23 Oct 1916, box 107, 420–15, General Board Subject Files 1900–47, RG 45, NA.

9. Assistant SECNAV Navy Yard Division to Commandant, Philadelphia Navy Yard, 15 May 1922, box 3141; Yarnell to Commandant, Philadelphia Navy Yard, #SS/S41–1(300320), 8 May 1930, box 4024, SECNAV GENCORR 1926–40, RG 80, NA.

10. The S–10 through 13 were the test vessels for the Bu-MAN engines.

11. Gear and Camshaft Reports on the S–16, 17, and 19, 6 Aug 1917, vol. 188 (Gray Binders), Bd I/S, RG 37, NA; Camshaft Noise Reports (S—34/SS—139), 6 Aug 1917, box 64, Reports of Material Inspection of Naval Vessels 1920–42, Bd I/S, RG 38, NA.

12. BUSENG to Inspector of Machinery, Groton, 23 May 1919, vol. 188 (Gray Binders, S–16, 17, and 19), Bd I/S, RG 38, NA.

13. Nelseco to Daniels, #27219–742, 17 Jun 1918, box 2162, SECNAV GENCORR 1916–26, RG 80, NA. For the details on the S-class engines, see Machinery and Hull Data for the S–32 (SS–137), 14 Feb 1923, box 63; Machinery and Hull Data for the S–3 (SS–107), 29–30 Jun 1919, box 2, Reports of the Material Inspection of Naval Vessels 1920–42, Bd I/S, RG 38, NA.

14. For example, Busch-Sulzer to Daniels, #27219–742, 15 Jun 1918, box 2162, SECNAV GENCORR 1916–26, RG 80, NA. These engines were for the S–14 through 17 (SS–119 through 122).

15. Mean effective pressure measures the average net pressure difference in pounds per square inch on the two sides of the piston in engines. This was only one indication that the German pistons and castings were able to withstand much higher pressures than American diesels could. For example, the mep for the MAN diesel slated for a U-boat minelayer was 83.6 psi as compared to 73 psi for the Nelseco and Busch-Sulzer engines powering the T–1 and the S–1 through S–3.

16. BUSENG to SECNAV, #C–3–956/1, 3 Mar 1919, box 2163, SECNAV GENCORR 1916–26, RG 80, NA.

17. Knapp to OPNAV, #28766–177:157, 9 Jul 1919, box 2767, SECNAV GENCORR 1916–26, RG 80, NA.

18. CNO (Submarine Section) to BUC&R, BUSENG, BUORD, #28766– 177:197, 8 Nov 1919, box 2767, SECNAV GENCORR 1916–26, RG 80, NA.

19. Submarine Officers Conference, 10 May 1920, Series 1, file 3, box 1, Subs/UWD, OA.

20. CAPT T. Hart to CNO, 11 Nov 1919, Series 1, file 3, box 1, Subs/UWD, OA.

21. The first published study illuminating the torsional vibration problem was F. M. Lewis, "Torsional Vibrations in the Diesel Engine." *SNAME Transactions XXXIII* (1925): 109–145.

22. When an engine was "rated," the Navy defined the basic performance characteristics it expected from the machine. This included the amount of power an engine could safely generate at different rpm levels. To re-rate an engine meant the Navy would receive the same diesel, but it lowered its performance expectations. In the case of the S-class this often meant that the surface speed would fall below the expected pace and the Navy would have to settle for something less than it desired when the contract was awarded.

23. C. F. Taylor, *Aircraft Propulsion*, Smithsonian Annals of Flight (Washington, 1971); Richard C. Knott, *The American Flying Boat* (Annapolis, 1979); Philip S. Dickey III, *The Liberty Engine, 1918–1942*, Smithsonian Annals of Flight (Washington, 1968).

24. Report of the Inspector of Machinery (Fore River Shipbuilding Company), 10 Apr 1920, box 1, Reports of the Material Inspection of Naval Vessels, Bd I/S, RG 38, NA.

25. Ibid.

26. Preliminary Trials of the S-4 (SS–109), 5 & 11 Nov 1920, box 2, Reports on the Material Inspection of Naval Vessels 1920–42, Bd I/S, RG 38, NA.

27. COMSUBFLOT 3 to CNO, #28729–103:3, 13 Sep 1920, subj: Performance of the Diesel-engine Plant of the USS S-one, box 2708, SECNAV GENCORR 1916–26, RG 80, NA.

28. Brake horsepower is the horse power measured by the force applied to a friction brake or by an absorption dynamometer attached to a shaft or flywheel. Put simply, it is the horsepower reading obtained when certain standard instruments, like a friction brake, are used to measure the power output of an engine.

29. CNO to SECNAV, #28729–159:2, 19 Apr 1921, box 2708, SECNAV GENCORR 1916–26, RG 80, NA.

30. BUSENG to SECNAV, #29035–44, 10 Apr 1920, box 3098, SECNAV GENCORR 1916–26, RG 80, NA.

31. Memo for the CNO (Admiral Coontz), #28729–103, 21 Sep 1920, box 2708, SECNAV GENCORR 1916–26, RG 80, NA.

32. Senior Member of the General Board to SECNAV, #28729–159:3, 6 Dec 1920, box 2708, SECNAV GENCORR 1916-26, RG 80, NA.

33. CNO to SECNAV, #28729–159:3, 19 Apr 1921, box 2708, SECNAV GENCORR 1916–26, RG 80, NA.

34. Memorandum "A," Machinery, S-type Submarines, #28729–159:1, 15 Dec 1920, box 2708, SECNAV GENCORR 1916–26, RG 80, NA.

35. EB to Assistant SECNAV Gordon Woodbury, #28816–45 through 84, 1 Dec 1920, box 2835, SECNAV GENCORR 1916–26, RG 80, NA.

36. CDR Guy Davis, Inspector of Machinery, Groton to BUENG, #28816–45–84, 4 Feb 1921, box 2835, SECNAV GENCORR 1916–26, RG 80, NA.

37. SECNAV to Compensation Board, #28816–45 through 84, 12 Feb 1921, box 2835, SECNAV GENCORR 1916–26, RG 80, NA.

38. Compensation Board to SECNAV via BUC&R and BUENG, #22816–45–83, 5 Mar 1921, box

2835, SECNAV GENCORR 1916–26, RG 80, NA.

39. EB Memo to Navy Department, #28816–32:92, 9 Mar 1921, box 2835, SECNAV GENCORR 1916–26, RG 80, NA.

40. Henry Carse, President of EB to Assistant SECNAV, #28816–45:2, 18 Mar 1921, box 2835, SECNAV GENCORR 1916–26, RG 80, NA.

41. Spear to Inspector of Machinery, Groton, 21 Mar 1921; Carse to SECNAV, 23 Mar 1921; Spear to Inspector of Machinery, Groton, #28816–84, 24 Mar 1921, box 2835, SECNAV GENCORR 1916–26, RG 80, NA.

42. BUENG to SECNAV, #28816–83, 26 Mar 1921, box 2835, SECNAV GENCORR 1916–26, RG 80, NA.

43. BUENG to SECNAV, #28816–92, 8 Apr 1921, box 2835, SECNAV GENCORR 1916–26, RG 80, NA.

44. SECNAV Edwin Denby to EB, #28729–197, 14 Feb 1922, box 2709, SECNAV GENCORR 1916–26, RG 80, NA. This document also outlines the various changes to the diesels mandated by BUENG in addition to the change in crankshaft size. The cost-plus-10-percent contracts allowed the contractor the freedom to negotiate for the best price for goods and services provided by a subcontractor, limiting the profit that the Navy permitted the firm to take to 10 percent of the cost of the boat. Fixed-price contracts required the contractor to follow Navy limits and pre-set prices for virtually every subcontract arrangement. EB absorbed its independent Nelseco facility in 1929, suffering from a lack of technical success and engine contracts at the opening of the Depression years.

45. Final Trial of the S–14 (SS–119), 17 Aug 1921, box 8; Preliminary Trial of the S–16 (SS–121), 28 Sep–7 Oct 1920, box 10; Preliminary Trials of the S–15 (SS–120), 26 Oct–15–20 Nov 1920, box 9, Reports of the Material Inspection of Naval Vessels, Bd I/S, RG 38, NA. See also Final Trial of the S–14 (SS–119), 17 Aug 1921, box 8; Preliminary Trial of the S–16 (SS–121), 28 Sep–7 Oct 1920, box 10, Reports of the Material Inspection of Naval Vessels, Bd I/S, RG 38, NA.

46. There were only three vessels of this class (T–1 through 3), and they became the precursors of the Navy's fleet submarines. Fore River Shipbuilding Company built them under contract to Electric Boat beginning with the T–1 in 1916 (commissioned 1920), and continuing with the T–2 and T–3 in 1917. The T–2 was commissioned in 1922, and the T–3 in 1920.

47. Bd I/S to CNO, #28575–350, 19 Nov 1921, box 2556, SECNAV GENCORR 1916–26, RG 80, NA.

48. Assistant SECNAV Roosevelt to EB, #29197–1, 28 May 1920, box 3145, SECNAV GENCORR 1916–26, RG 80, NA; "List of concerns to whom proposals for the machinery of Fleet Submarines should be sent," #29197–1, 12 Aug 1920, box 3145, SECNAV GENCORR 1916–26, RG 80, NA.

49. CNO (Submarine Section) to CNO, #29035–51, 29 Jun 1920, box 3098, SECNAV GENCORR 1916–26, RG 80, NA.

50. "List of Diesel Motors for Submarines Sold Abroad," #28766– 306:23, 18 May 1921, box 2768, SECNAV GENCORR 1916–26, RG 80, NA.

51. CAPT G. A. Williams (Submarine Section), Memo for the CNO, 15 Mar 1921, Series 1, file 3, box 1, Subs/UWD, OA. The diesels slated for the U–127 were six-cylinder, four-stroke models produced by MAN. Erich Gröner, *Die deutschen Kriegschiffe 1815–1945* (Munich, 1966), p. 357.

52. LCDR E. D. McWhorter, Memo for the Chief of BUENG, #28747–321, 27 Jan 1922, box 2720, SECNAV GENCORR 1916–26, RG 80, NA.

53. CAPT Charles T. Vogelgesang, Commandant, New York Navy Yard to SECNAV, #28747–324, 20 Feb 1922, box 2720, SECNAV GENCORR 1916–26, RG 80, NA.

54. BUENG to CO USS S–10 and S–11 via Commandant, New York Navy Yard, #28747–365, 19 Jan 1923, box 2720, SECNAV GENCORR 1916–26, RG 80, NA; BUENG to CNO (Director of

Submarines), #28747–359 29 Dec 1922, box 2720, SECNAV GENCORR 1916–26, RG 80, NA. In 1929 Rear Admiral Yarnell praised the Bu-MAN as the best submarine diesel in the world. If this was an exaggeration, it was still an accomplishment that "the S-12 has cruised over 6,000 miles per engine casualty, which compares favorably with battleship records." (Cruiser Submarines, V–7, V–8, and V–9—Preliminary Design, 15 Aug 1929, General Board Hearings of 1929, vol. 1, p. 194, Scholarly Resources Microfilm, OA.)

55. LCDR C. Q. Wright, USS S–10 to CNO via Submarine Division Zero and Submarine Divisions Atlantic, #28747–359, 19 Dec 1922, box 2720, SECNAV GENCORR 1916–26, RG 80, NA. Submarine Division Zero, located at Key West, performed testing functions for the technical bureaus. It was not an operational command.

56. Testimony of Rear Admiral J. K. Robison, Chief of BUENG, 2 Apr 1923, pp. 80ff., vol. 1, General Board Hearings of 1923, Scholarly Resources Microfilm, OA. For Robison's comments on the size of the engine versus the capacity of the submarine and the consequences of this conflict, see pages 120ff.

57. BUENG to CNO, #28575–428, 10 Dec 1924; CNO to BUENG, #28575–442, 14 Sep 1925; BUENG to CNO, #28575–448, 8 Jan 1926, box 2556, SECNAV GENCORR 1916–26, RG 80, NA.

58. The Lake Torpedo Boat Company, which built the S–14 through 17, went out of business in 1924. Therefore these boats were left under the complete control of the Navy for a major overhaul such as this one. In most cases the original contractor usually participated in this work even though the vessel was commissioned. If other S-class boats had become involved, Electric Boat would have certainly taken part, as it did in a number of re-engining and overhaul projects during the interwar years. Lake had installed Busch-Sulzer engines in the S–14 through 17 in 1918–1919. Mare Island Naval Shipyard replaced these diesels in 1926–1927 with MAN engines purchased from Germany by the Navy via EB. U.S. Submarine S–16 (SS–121), 7 Jun 1928, box 9, Reports of the Material Inspection of Naval Vessels 1920–43, Bd I/S, RG 38, NA.

59. Testimony of Captain Ormond L. Cox, 1 Dec 1927, pp. 143ff., vol. 2, General Board Hearings of 1927, Scholarly Resources Microfilm, OA.

60. JAG to SECNAV, n.d. 1930, Ship Construction Folder, box 22, Assistant SECNAV Alpha Files, RG 80, NA.

61. Submarines V–7, V–8, and V–9, Design of, 7 Apr 1930, General Board Hearings of 1930, vol. 1, pp. 107ff., Scholarly Resources Microfilm, OA.

62. Testifying before the General Board on 8 July 1930, Yarnell reported on his meeting with Herr Dr. Lauster, one of MAN's wartime designers, as well as the excellence of the product he encountered. "Main Engines and Necessary Auxiliaries for the USS V–8 and USS V–9," 8 Jul 1930, General Board Hearings of 1930, vol. 1, pp. 253ff., Scholarly Resources Microfilm, OA; Yarnell to CNO, 6 May 1931, box 209, Office of SECNAV Confidential Correspondence 1927–1939, RG 80, NA.

63. Statement of Rear Admiral H. E. Yarnell, Chief of the Bureau of Engineering, 12 Jan 1931, *Sundry Legislation Affecting the Naval Establishment, 1930-1931: Hearings before the Committee on Naval Affairs of the House of Representatives,* 71st Cong., 3d sess., 1931, p. 3610.

64. BUENG had to wait until December of 1931 to get the $3 million through Congress. The appropriation was not made in the third session in spite of support from the Secretary of the Navy and the White House's director of the budget. The money was used to good purpose by Yarnell's successor at BUENG, Rear Admiral S. M. Robinson, who assumed command at BUENG in May 1931. The Navy Department wasted no time in determining how the money should be spent, if allocated. It solicited opinions from the members of the Submarine Officers Conference on the best and most effective way of using the money. See CNO form letter soliciting opinions on best use of the $3 million submarine diesel R&D appropriation, 29 Jan 1931, Series 1, file 5, box 4, Subs/UWD, OA.

65. Submarine Engines, 24 Apr 1930, 420–15, box 111, General Board Subject Files 1900–47, RG 80, NA.

66. Memo for Acting SECNAV, 28 Mar 1930, 420–15, box 111, General Board Subject Files 1900–47, RG 80, NA.

67. The Development of Improved Diesel Motive Power for the U.S. Navy, n.d. (probably 1931), Series 1, file 5, box 4, Subs/UWD, OA; "Main Engines and Necessary Auxiliaries for the USS V–8 and USS V–9," 8 Jul 1930, General Board Hearings of 1930, vol. 1, pp. 253ff., Scholarly Resources Microfilm, OA.

68. Acting SECNAV Ingalls to Cochran, 7 Mar 1931; BUENG to JAG, 13 Mar 1931; F. Joerger (MAN) to JAG, 24 Jun 1931; BUENG to JAG, 28 Sep 1931; JAG to Joerger, 28 Sep 1931, #SS/S41–3(310307), box 4024, SECNAV GENCORR 1926–40, RG 80, NA.

69. "Main Engines and Necessary Auxiliaries for the USS V–8 and USS V–9," 8 Jul 1930, General Board Hearings of 1930, vol. 1, p. 257, Scholarly Resources Microfilm, OA.

70. Dietrich Freiherr von Lassberg, "Augsburger MAN Dieselmotoren," Historisches Archiv, MAN AG, Augsburg.

71. The term "motor" is used to denote an electric motor as opposed to a diesel "engine."

72. Lockwood, *Down to the Sea in Subs*, p. 161.

73. CO USS S–14 to COMSUBDIV 18, 11 Feb 1928, box 8, Reports of Material Inspection of Naval Vessels 1920–42, Bd I/S, RG 38, NA. Excessive temperatures, as well as a lack of faith in the machinery on the part of the operating personnel, caused the same results in April 1928 when the division tested DED cruising en route to Coco Solo. See CNO to Commander Control Force, 17 Apr 1928, box 8, Reports of Material Inspections of Naval Vessels 1920–42, Bd I/S, RG 38, NA.

74. Inspection of the USS S–16 at Key West, 7 Jun 1928, box 9, Reports of the Material Inspection of Naval Vessels, Bd I/S, RG 38, NA.

75. "Characteristics of Future Submarines—Recommendations," 31 Oct 1928, General Board Hearings of 1928, vol. 2, pp. 16ff., Scholarly Resources Microfilm, OA.

76. Battery Explosion in the E–2—Opinion of the Court of Inquiry, #26283–988:7, 16 Feb 1916, box 1753, SECNAV GENCORR 1916–26, RG 80, NA.

77. "Electric Boat Company's Submarine Design No. 140–A," 23 Jul 1929, General Board Hearings of 1929, vol. 1, pp. 161–62, Scholarly Resources Microfilm, OA.

78. "Cruiser Submarines V–7, V–8, and V–9—Preliminary Designs," 15 Aug 1929, General Board Hearings of 1929, vol. 1, pp. 188–94, Scholarly Resources Microfilm, OA.

79. FM engine, 1934: Eight-cylinder, two-cycle, opposed-piston, two-crankshaft unit.

80. HOR engine, 1934: MAN, double-acting, two-cycle, eight-cylinder type. For information on the engine competition and the HOR connection with MAN, see Diesel Engines for Modern U.S. Submarines, n.d. (probably 1936), box 112, 420–15, General Board Subject Files 1900–47, RG 80, NA; von Lassberg, "Augsburger M.A.N.-Dieselmotoren", p. 191. HOR powered not only the SS–181 but also the SS–182 through 184, SS–188 through 190, SS–194, and SS–253 through 264.

81. The reduction gear is the transmission employed to reduce the high revolutions of the electric motors to a rate sufficient to drive the boat without causing shaft damage or propeller cavitation.

82. John D. Alden, "Development of the High Speed Diesel Engine for United States Submarines," *Naval Engineers Journal* 91 (Aug 1979): 43-49; Bd I/S to CNO, #SS182/S8(390325), 10 Jul 1929, BUENG to JAG, #SS182–4/S8 (3–20–Bc), 24 May 1939, box 4112, SECNAV GENCORR 1926–40, RG 80, NA.

83. The interwar Navy also learned the importance of contract language and the selective application of fixed-price and cost-plus contracts both to define better the product in question

and to monitor its cost and progress. Without more precise terms, a clear definition of expectations, and a contract suited to the project the Navy could easily drive its only major contractor out of the submarine business altogether.

6. Conclusions

1. Charles Lockwood to Francis Low, 17 May 1940, Series 4, file 8, box 14, Subs/UWD, OA.

2. United States Fleet Problem 7 (Mar 1927), 8 (Apr 1928), and 13 (Mar 1932), Microfilm reels 9, 11, and 14, Records Relating to U.S. Navy Fleet Problems, M964, RG 38, Navy Department Library; Michael A. Palmer, "Undersea Warfare and Maritime Strategy: The American Experience" (Paper delivered at the Undersea Dimension of Maritime Strategy Conference, Halifax, Nova Scotia, 22 Jun 1989); Talbott, "Weapons Development, War Planning and Policy," pp. 53-71; Bemis, "Submarine Warfare in the Strategy of American Defense and Diplomacy, 1915–1945," Unpublished MMS, OA.

3. The author owes the general analysis of the relationship between German and American industry to a conversation with and presentation by Professor Volker Berghahn of Brown University, which took place at the German Historical Institute in Washington, D.C., on 9 February 1989. Professor Berghahn's paper was entitled "Germany and America—The Industrial Connection, 1918–1970."

Bibliography

Building American Submarines, 1914–1940, is based on a wealth of unpublished primary sources from a variety of archives. These sources provide a firm foundation for this first examination of the naval-industrial relationship governing submarine construction.

The most valuable records employed here came from the General Correspondence collections of the Secretary of the Navy and the Bureaus of Construction and Repair and Engineering, as well as those of the General Board of the Navy, the Board of Inspection and Survey, the Compensation Board, the Submarine Board, and Assistant Secretary of the Navy Charles Edison's Alpha (Alphabetical) File, among others, held at the National Archives. These and other naval records collections provide the only store of relatively complete correspondence between the Navy and its contractors. The bureaus and other offices saved not only their own outgoing correspondence, but also the letters received from the firms with which the Navy did business.

Other important sources include the Sperry Company Records at the Hagley Museum, the Technical Library of the Electric Boat Division, General Dynamics Corporation, the Holland and Electric Boat collections at the Submarine Force Library and Museum, as well as the Strategic Plans and Undersea Warfare Division Files at the U.S. Navy's Operational Archives.

Published sources treating the interaction between the Navy and the submarine industry during this period are virtually nonexistent. This study should promote some additional scholarship and historical debate. The published primary and secondary works that contributed most to the present study deal with mobilization, personal biography, and the best current interpretations of the naval-industrial complex.

There are a number of excellent works on American industry and the Navy during the First World War. Of these, the first-hand accounts prepared by contemporaries Bernard M. Baruch and Grosvenor Clarkson provide the insider's view of American wartime industry and government. Robert D. Cuff's history of the War Industries Board complements these sources with an excellent perspective on the agency created to place America's economy on a war footing.

Unfortunately, these works are not complemented by an insightful history of the American submarine force in the First World War. The only account of American submarine operations in the Great War is a two-part article by Carroll S. Alden that appeared in the United States Naval Institute *Proceedings* in 1920. Alden's work gives an excellent account of the routine activities of the Navy's submarine force operating along the American coast and from their European wartime bases in the Azores in the east central Atlantic, and Bantry Bay, Ireland.

In the process Professor Alden provides little insight into the strategy that motivated these activities. Much of his account depends on direct and lengthy quotations from war diaries and deck logs. These give the flavor of submarine operations but the work provides no analysis that might deepen the reader's appreciation of submarine performance, or the construction and support functions of industry. Thus American submarine operations during the First World War is an important subject still sorely in need of historical evaluation within the context provided by Clarkson, Baruch, and Cuff, among others.

Most of the source material for the commentary on strategy that appears in this work comes from archival sources, some of which have already inspired seminal secondary works on submarine strategy. In his unpublished analysis of the American decision to wage unrestricted submarine warfare against the Japanese in the Second World War, Samuel Flagg Bemis demonstrated that this strategy was not spontaneous, but had definite antecedents. These ideas motivated the historian James E. Talbott to further develop Bemis's thesis that this type of warfare did not suddenly become part of American strategy after the Japanese attack on 7 December 1941. Talbott argues that this decision had roots in naval thinking that ran deeper than even Bemis's work revealed. These two scholars have laid to rest the notion that unrestricted submarine warfare simply sprang from a desire to avenge Pearl Harbor.

Memoirs and biographies contributed personal insights into the construction program and the evolution of strategy and design. The best of these include Vice Admiral Charles A. Lockwood's *Down to the Sea in Subs*, and the biography of Admiral Thomas C. Hart by James Leutze. The former provides the perspective of a submarine operator and strategist often frustrated with the restrictions placed upon U.S. submarine operations as late as 1940. The latter offers considerable insight into the American desire, which emerged during the interwar debates on submarine strategy and design, to emulate the German U-boats of the First World War. The autobiography of Vice Admiral Harold G. Bowen, *Ships, Machinery, and Mossbacks*, offers excellent first-hand technical insights into the diesel engine problems plaguing the Bureau of Engineering and the submarine community during the interwar years.

Studies by Robert A. Hoover, Raymond G. O'Connor, and Lawrence H. Douglas furnished the political and international side of the postwar debate on the use of the submarine. Their works on the major disarmament conferences of the interwar period illustrate the difficulty of reaching an international agreement on submarine control and provide an examination of the few restrictions imposed on submarine builders in the signatory countries. The London Conference of 1930 limited the American, British, and Japanese navies to 52,700 tons of submarines each, but none of the disarmament conferences succeeded in abolishing the vessels as a type. The British supported abolition because the submarine posed the greatest possible threat to the tenuous postwar mastery of the seas held by the Royal Navy.

Although they do not treat the American submarine industry in particular, a number of excellent sources on other aspects of the naval-industrial relationship contributed to a deeper understanding of the present topic. This study has benefitted from the work done by Dean C. Allard and Benjamin Franklin Cooling on the American iron and steel industry. Their examination of the various conflicts between the Navy, industry, and Congress provide an excellent perspective on the role of such confrontations in the development of a working relationship between the Navy and industry. A reading of Paul Koistinen's *The Military Industrial Complex, A Historical Perspective* and the collection of essays entitled *War, Business, and American Society*, edited by Cooling, furnish a superb overview of this phenomenon for the 1914–1940 period. In addition, William McNeill's *Pursuit of Power* advanced the concept of command technology, used here to describe the early relationship between the Navy and industry that had not yet matured into the naval-industrial complex.

Primary Sources

Archival and Special Collections

National Archives, Washington, DC.

    Record Group 19:
        General Correspondence of the Bureau of Steam Engineering, 1911–1922
        Confidential Correspondence Regarding Research and Design of Radio and other Communications Apparatus
        General Correspondence of the Bureau of Construction and Repair (BUC&R), 1925–1940
        BUC&R Correspondence Regarding Ships, 1916–1925
        BUC&R Repair and Design Data for U.S. Naval Vessels, 1914–1927
        BUC&R Research Data, 1913–1937
        Board on Submarine Claims, 1918–1922

    Record Group 38:
        Board of Inspection and Survey (Reports of the Material Inspection of Naval Vessels)

    Record Group 45:
        General Board Subject Files, 1900–1947

    Record Group 80:
        General Correspondence of the Secretary of the Navy, 1916–1926 and 1926–1940
        Compensation Board
        Records of Secretary of the Navy James Forrestal, 1940–1947
        Assistant Secretary of the Navy Alpha File
        Naval Consulting Board Correspondence Files, 1915–1923
        Secretary of the Navy Confidential Correspondence, 1927–1939

Washington National Records Center, Suitland, MD.

    Record Group 19:
        Bureau of Ships General Correspondence, 1940–1945
        Bureau of Engineering General Correspondence, 1910–1940

U.S. Navy Operational Archives, Naval Historical Center, Washington, DC.

    Hearings of the General Board of the Navy (Microfilm)

    Strategic Plans Division Records

    Submarines—Undersea Warfare Division Records

Samuel Flagg Bemis. "Submarine Warfare in the Strategy of American Defense and Diplomacy, 1915–1945." Unpublished MSS.

Interviews and Oral Histories:

> Land, Emory S. Interview with John T. Mason, Jr. 30 January 1963. Columbia University Oral History Project, New York, NY.
>> Leonard, John S. Interview with author. 25 September 1989. Naval Historical Center.
>>> Jackson, Harry. Interview with author. 24 September 1989. Naval Historical Center.

Submarine Force Library and Museum, Groton, CT

Holland Collection

Electric Boat Collection (Individual Submarine Historical Files)

Technical Library and Records Vault, Electric Boat Division, General Dynamics Corporation, Groton, CT

"History of the Electric Boat Company." Unpublished Typescript.

Drawing Books

Pattern Books

Electrical Sketches

Hull Plan Lists

Hagley Museum Archives, Wilmington, DE.

Elmer Sperry Papers

Sperry Company Records

Historisches Museum, MAN AG, Augsburg, Federal Republic of Germany

Dietrich Freiherr von Lassberg, "Augsburger M.A.N. Dieselmotoren"

Published Primary Sources

Baruch, Bernard M. *American Industry in the War: A Report of the War Industries Board*. Washington: GPO, 1921.

Bowen, Harold G. *Ships, Machinery, and Mossbacks*. Princeton, NJ: Princeton University Press, 1954.

Cable, Frank T. *The Birth and Development of the American Submarine*. New York: Harper and Brothers, 1924.

Clarkson, Grosvenor B. *Industrial America in the World War: The Strategy Behind The Line, 1917-1918*. Boston: Houghton Mifflin Co., 1923.

Historical Section, Navy Department. *History of the Bureau of Engineering, Navy Department, during the World War*. Washington: GPO, 1922.

Lake, Simon. *The Submarine in War and Peace*. Philadelphia: J. P. Lippincott Co., 1918.

Lockwood, Charles A. *Down to the Sea in Subs*. New York: W. W. Norton & Co., 1967.

U.S. Congress. House. *Sundry Legislation Affecting the Naval Establishment, 1930–1931: Hearings before the Committee on Naval Affairs of the House of Representatives*. 71st Cong., 3d sess. 1931.

U.S. Congress. Senate. *Munitions Industry: Report of the Special Committee on Investigation of the Munitions Industry*, 74th Cong., 1st. sess. 1936. S. Res. 206.

U.S. Department of the Navy. *Annual Report of the Navy Department*. Washington: 1914–1940.

Secondary Sources

Books

Alden, John D. *The Fleet Submarine in the U.S. Navy: A Design and Construction History*. Annapolis: Naval Institute Press, 1979.

Brown, David T. *A History of the Sulzer Low-Speed Marine Diesel Engine*. Winterthur, Switzerland: Sulzer Brothers, Ltd., 1984.

Carey, Omer L., ed. *The Military Industrial Complex and U.S. Foreign Policy*. Pullman, WA: Washington State University Press, 1969.

Cocker, M. P. *Observer's Directory of Royal Naval Submarines*. Annapolis: Naval Institute Press, 1982.

Cooling, Benjamin Franklin. *Gray Steel and Blue Water Navy*. Hamden, CT: Archon Books, 1979.

Cooling, Benjamin Franklin, ed. *War, Business, and American Society*. Port Washington, NY: Kennikat Press, 1977.

Cuff, Robert D. *The War Industries Board: Business-Government Relations during World War I*. Baltimore: Johns Hopkins University Press, 1973.

Davis, George T. *A Navy Second to None*. New York: Harcourt, Brace, and Co., 1940.

Dickey, Philip S. III. *The Liberty Engine, 1918–1942*. Smithsonian Annals of Flight. Washington: Smithsonian Institution Press, 1968.

Friedman, Norman. *Submarine Design and Development*. Annapolis: Naval Institute Press, 1984.

Furer, Julius Augustus. *Administration of the Navy Department in World War II*. Washington: Department of the Navy, 1959.

Gebhard, Louis A. *Evolution of Radio-Electronics and Contributions of the Naval Research Laboratory*. Washington: Naval Research Lab, 1979.

Gröner, Erich. *Die deutschen Kriegschiffe 1815–1945*. Munich: J. F. Lehmanns Verlag, 1966.

Hackmann, Willem. *Seek and Strike: Sonar, Anti-Submarine Warfare and the Royal Navy, 1914–54*. London: HMSO, 1984.

Harrington, Roy L., ed. *Marine Engineering*. New York: Society of Naval Architects and Marine Engineers, 1971.

Hoover, Robert A. *Arms Control: The Interwar Naval Limitation Agreements*. Denver, CO: Graduate School of International Studies, 1980.

Jenkins, Ernest H. *A History of the French Navy*. London: Macdonald and Jane's, 1973.

Jolie, E. W. *A Brief History of U.S. Navy Torpedo Development*. Newport, RI: Naval Underwater Systems Center, 1978.

Knott, Captain Richard C. USN. *The American Flying Boat*. Annapolis: Naval Institute Press, 1979.

Koistinen, Paul. *The Military-Industrial Complex, A Historical Perspective*. New York: Praeger, 1980.

Kollmorgen Corporation. *The Submarine Periscope, 1916–1966*. Northhampton, MA: Kollmorgen Corp., 1966.

Leutze, James. *A Different Kind of Victory: A Biography of Admiral Thomas C. Hart*. Annapolis: Naval Institute Press, 1981.

Lipscomb, F. W. *The British Submarine*. Greenwich: Conway Maritime Press, 1975.

Manchester, William. *The Arms of Krupp*. Boston: Little, Brown and Company, 1968.

McNeill, William H. *The Pursuit of Power*. Chicago: University of Chicago Press, 1982.

Morison, Elting E. *Men, Machines, and Modern Times*. Cambridge, MA: M.I.T. Press, 1966.

Morris, Richard K. *John P. Holland: Inventor of the Modern Submarine*. Annapolis: Naval Institute Press, 1966.

Naval History Division. *Dictionary of American Naval Fighting Ships*. 8 vols. Washington: GPO, 1964.

O'Connor, Raymond G. *Perilous Equilibrium: The United States and the London Naval Conference of 1930*. Lawrence: University of Kansas Press, 1962.

Paullin, Charles O. *Paullin's History of Naval Administration, 1775–1911*. Annapolis: Naval Institute Press, 1968.

Polmar, Norman. *The American Submarine*. Annapolis: Nautical and Aviation Publishing Company of America, 1981.

Ropp, Theodore. *The Development of a Modern Navy: French Naval Policy, 1871–1904.* Annapolis: Naval Institute Press, 1987.

Ranft, Bryan, ed. *Technical Change and British Naval Policy, 1860–1939.* London: Hodder and Stoughton, 1977.

Rössler, Eherhard. *Geschichte des deutschen Ubootbaus.* Munich: J. F. Lehmanns Verlag, 1975.

Sumida, Jon Tetsuro. *In Defense of Naval Supremacy, Finance, Technology, and British Naval Policy, 1889–1914.* Boston: Unwin Hyman, 1989.

Taylor, C. Fayette. *Aircraft Propulsion.* Smithsonian Annals of Flight. Washington: Smithsonian Institution Press, 1971.

Walker, Bruce H. *Periscopes, People, and Progress.* North Adams, MA: Excelsior Printing, 1984.

Weir, Gary E. *Building the Kaiser's Navy: The Imperial Naval Office and German Industry in the Tirpitz Era, 1890–1919.* Annapolis: Naval Institute Press, forthcoming 1991.

Articles

Alden, Carroll S. "American Submarine Operations in the War" United States Naval Institute *Proceedings* 46 (June-July 1920): 1–40; 41–76.

Alden, John D. "Development of the High Speed Diesel Engine for United States Submarines," *Naval Engineers Journal*, 91 (August 1979): 43–49.

Henry, David. "British Submarine Policy, 1918–1939." In *Technical Change and British Naval Policy, 1860–1939*, pp. 80–107. Edited by Bryan Ranft. London: Hodder and Stoughton, 1977.

Huntington, Samuel P. "The Defense Establishment: Vested Interests and the Public Interest." In *The Military Industrial Complex and U. S. Foreign Policy*, pp. 562–84. Edited by Omer L. Carey. Pullman, WA: Washington State University Press, 1969.

Lasky, Marvin. "A Historical Review of Underwater Acoustic Technology 1916–1939 with Emphasis on Undersea Warfare." *U.S. Navy Journal of Underwater Acoustics* 24 (October 1974): 597–624.

Lewis, F. M. "Torsional Vibrations in the Diesel Engine." *Society of Naval Architects and Marine Engineers Transactions XXXIII* (1925): 109–145.

Talbott, James E. "Weapons Development, War Planning and Policy: The U. S. Navy and the Submarine, 1917–1941." *Naval War College Review* 37 (May-June 1984): 53–71.

Wechsler, Laskar. "Medium and High Speed Diesel Engines." In *Marine Engineering*, pp. 246–79. Edited by Roy L. Harrington. New York: Society of Naval Architects and Marine Engineers, 1971.

Papers

Allard, Dean C. "The Influence of the United States Navy Upon the American Steel Industry, 1880–1900." M.A., Georgetown University, 1959.

Douglas, Lawrence H. "Submarine Disarmament: 1919–1936." Ph.D. Diss., Syracuse University, 1969.

West, Michael A. "Laying the Legislative Foundation: The House Naval Affairs Committee and the Construction of the Treaty Navy, 1926–1934." Ph.D. Diss., Ohio State University, 1980.

Index